PSYCHOLOGICAL ASPECTS
OF STRESS

PSYCHOLOGICAL ASPECTS OF STRESS

Edited by

HARRY S. ABRAM

Associate Professor of Psychiatry
University of Virginia School of Medicine
Charlottesville, Virginia

CHARLES C THOMAS • PUBLISHER
Springfield · Illinois · U.S.A.

Published and Distributed throughout the world by
CHARLES C THOMAS · PUBLISHER
BANNERSTONE HOUSE
301-327 East Lawrence Avenue, Springfield, Illinois, U.S.A.
NATCHEZ PLANTATION HOUSE
735 North Atlantic Boulevard, Fort Lauderdale, Florida, U.S.A.

© *1970, by* CHARLES C THOMAS · PUBLISHER
Library of Congress Catalog Card Number: 73-111664

With THOMAS BOOKS *careful attention is given to all details of
manufacturing and design. It is the Publisher's desire to present books
that are satisfactory as to their physical qualities and artistic possibilities
and appropriate for their particular use. THOMAS BOOKS will be true
to those laws of quality that assure a good name and good will.*

Printed in the United States of America
Y-2

CONTRIBUTORS

Peter G. Bourne, M.D.
Department of Psychiatry
Emory University
Atlanta, Georgia

N. H. Cassem, M.D.
Department of Psychiatry
Massachusetts General Hospital
Boston, Massachusetts

Paul Chodoff, M.D.
Clinical Professor of Psychiatry
George Washington University
School of Medicine
Washington, D.C.

Albert J. Glass, M.D.
Director
Oklahoma State Department of Mental Health
Oklahoma City, Oklahoma

Thomas P. Hackett, M.D.
Department of Psychiatry
Massachusetts General Hospital
Boston, Massachusetts

E. J. McLaughlin, Ph.D.
Space Medicine, Manned Space Flight
National Aeronautics and Space Administration
Washington, D.C.

Ian Stevenson, M.D.
Alumni Professor of Psychiatry
University of Virginia School of Medicine
Charlottesville, Virginia

FOREWORD

THE contents of this edition are composed of the six presentations given at the University of Virginia, April 23 to 24, 1969. At that time the University of Virginia School of Medicine and Medical Education for National Defense (MEND) jointly sponsored a symposium bearing the title of this volume. My introduction for the conference defines its scope and purpose:

> This symposium [originally entitled "Psychological Aspects of Catastrophic Events" and then abbreviated to its present title] examines and discusses man's response to stressful events in his life and environment, both of a pathological and physiological nature. Twentieth century life presents to modern man numerous situations in which he must react individually or as a member of a group to extremes of tension and anxiety. Thus we believe it both appropriate and timely that a conference be organized to focus attention on psychological response to such situations as man's reaction to outer space, life-threatening illness, concentration camps, combat, and disasters. Hopefully it will be an informative and stimulating one with free and active discussion among all involved.

Because of the high quality of each presentation, their relevance and the enthusiastic response of the audience, I think it is most appropriate and fitting that a wider reading audience share the information and impressions included in these six presentations.

I should also like to recognize the National Institute of Mental Health, Wyeth Laboratories, Hoffmann-LaRoche, Inc., and Merck Sharpe and Dohme for their support of the program and Miss Nancy Dunham for her secretarial assistance in preparing and organizing the symposium.

HARRY S. ABRAM, M.D.

CONTENTS

PSYCHOLOGICAL ASPECTS OF STRESS

Chapter 1

PRECOGNITIONS OF DISASTERS

IAN STEVENSON

THE word "disaster" commonly refers to serious accidents or misfortunes affecting (usually fatally) large numbers of persons. Before I discuss precognitions of such events with multiple fatalities, I must first review at some length the evidence for precognition in general. It will be seen along the way that most of the evidence for spontaneous precognitions concerns misfortunes to one person only and also that many of the events apparently precognized are disasters in that they involve deaths, serious accidents, and illnesses to the individual persons affected. I shall also make a brief excursion into theoretical aspects of precognition in which I shall not attempt to discuss this topic at length but will only indicate some of the important issues and direct the reader to more detailed discussions already published.

The word "precognition" refers to noninferential knowledge of the future. This definition excludes awareness of the possibility of future events from *conscious* knowledge of one's own, or other persons', intentions or from material conditions that, unless interrupted, will result in certain future events. The definition is not entirely satisfactory because, as we shall see, one theory of apparent precognition supposes that the percipient acquires knowledge of other persons' information or intentions by paranormal means, that is, by extrasensory perception, and then makes inferences (usually subconsciously) about the future from this knowledge.

Note: The author wishes to thank Dr. J. G. Pratt and Mrs. L. A. Dale for reading this paper and offering helpful suggestions for its improvement.

3

It should be helpful if I summarize a typical spontaneous pre-cognitive experience. I take my illustration from the biography of Mark Twain by Albert Bigelow Paine (25, p. 134 *et seq.*)

> When Mark Twain was a young man of about twenty, he and his brother Henry worked on a Mississippi riverboat running between St. Louis and New Orleans. One night when Mark Twain was sleeping at his sister's house in St. Louis he had the following vivid dream:
>
> > He saw Henry, a corpse, lying in a metallic burial case in the sitting room, supported on two chairs. On his breast lay a bouquet of flowers, with a single crimson bloom in the center.
>
> When Mark Twain awoke in the morning the dream had been so vivid that he believed his brother had died and when he rose and dressed, he thought he would go into his sister's sitting room and look at his dead brother. But he changed his mind and decided to go for a walk instead. He had walked to the middle of the block when he suddenly realized he had only dreamed that his brother was dead. He returned to the house and told the dream to his sister.
>
> A few weeks later, however, Mark Twain and his brother separated in New Orleans and returned towards St. Louis on separate ships. Four boilers of the *Pennsylvania*, the ship Henry was on, blew up with an enormous loss of life. Henry was badly injured and after a few days of terrible suffering, he died in Memphis, Tennessee. Although most of the victims of this disaster were buried in simple wooden coffins, some ladies of Memphis had become specially moved by the plight of the youthful Henry Clemens and they subscribed for a metal coffin for him. When Mark Twain went to see his brother's corpse laid out with the others, he found it in a metal coffin just as he had seen it in his dream, but without any bouquet of flowers. As he stood by the coffin, a lady entered and placed on the breast of Henry's body a bouquet of white flowers with one red rose in the center.

I said this case was typical and it is so because the apparent precognition occurred in a vivid dream, it concerned a close relative of the dreamer, the theme was death, and it contained verified details that no one could have rationally foreseen at the time of the dream. It also contained an important discrepancy between the details of the dream and the fulfilling event in that the coffin was seen in the dream to be in the sister's sitting room in St. Louis whereas Henry Clemens died in Memphis, Tennessee, and it was there that Mark Twain saw the metallic coffin with flowers on his brother's breast. Otherwise, everything was exactly as in his dream. Such discrepancies between dream and actual events occur commonly in precognitions.

THE EVIDENCE FOR PRECOGNITION

The evidence for precognition comes from two principal sources: spontaneous experiences, such as Mark Twain's dream, and laboratory experiments. Spontaneous experiences suggestive of precognition have been recorded since ancient times, but their systematic collection and analysis dates only from the founding of the (English) Society for Psychical Research (S.P.R.) in 1882. Since that time, however, a large number of cases has been carefully studied and published. The S.P.R. and its American counterpart, the American Society for Psychical Research, have published many well-documented reports of cases of ostensible precognition, (7, 9, 13, 15, 19, 34, 37). Sidgwick (37), Saltmarsh (34), Green (12), and Nicol (24) published summaries and analyses of some of the cases collected by the S.P.R. since 1882.

A good many cases of ostensible precognition can be readily explained along normal lines. In some instances, especially those containing few details, chance coincidence seems a likely explanation of the correspondence between the alleged precognition and the related events. However, in the majority of cases published in the scientific literature of parapsychology, the number of details corresponding between the subject's experience and the related events permits us to doubt that chance coincidence is a reasonable explanation. Experience and related event are often each unique and yet have so many unusual and corresponding details that the one seems almost a facsimile of the other. The resemblance strongly suggests some causal connection between the experience and the related events.

In other cases, errors of memory or "pseudo-presentiments," as Royce (32) called them, may lead a person to believe after an event has happened that he had some foreknowledge of it when in fact he did not. In others, the percipient may bring about an apparent fulfillment of a precognitive dream or vision by his own actions. In still others the ostensible precognition may have a suggestive effect on the subject that implements the occurrence of the seemingly predicted events. This might be the explanation for one well-known case in which a woman dreamed that she was pursued by a monkey in a London street. The next day she saw a monkey (which was certainly an unusual sight) on a street in London. The memory of her dream caused her to cry out, "My dream, my dream!" and this attracted the monkey's attention so that it began to follow her, thus "fulfilling" the dream (22, pp. 488-9). Still another, although probably rare, normal cause of ostensible precognitions is hyperesthesia. A subject may become subliminally aware of defective machinery, frayed ropes, small amounts of smoke, or other indices of some present or imminent accident. These stimuli may evoke a conscious awareness presented in the form of a prediction that is soon thereafter fulfilled. In a particularly dramatic case reported from Japan, a villager dreamed in the middle of the night that a tidal wave was going to wash over his village. He awoke and alerted the other residents of the village who escaped to safety before a tidal wave arrived later that day. In such a case, however, one can readily understand that a change in the wind, preceding the tidal wave by several hours, may have stimulated the dream.

Most of the cases in the scientific literature of parapsychology were reviewed with regard to such normal explanations before publication, and they are nearly always accompanied by supporting documents. The report usually includes a firsthand statement by the percipient and a corroborating statement by someone who testifies that the percipient told him about his dream or other experience before either of them had normal knowledge of the related events; in addition, independent statements from other persons or relevant newspaper reports verify the related events and give their date and place of occurrence.* Most of the published cases therefore seem inexplicable along normal lines and call for some other explanation. It is the resistance of these cases to normal explanations that brings them into the field of parapsychological investigations.

---

*Incidentally, the case of Mark Twain that I cited earlier is not typical of cases published in the parapsychological literature. It was not recorded until many years after it happened and Mark Twain's biographer did not furnish any corroborating or verifying documents. I deliberately cited this case, however (instead of one of the many better documented ones), in order to emphasize that many experiences of this kind happen to ordinary people and a considerable number have been reported more or less casually in biographies, reminiscences, and similar works.

However, spontaneous cases in parapsychology rarely provide the opportunity for the kinds of observation and documentation which would permit a firm exclusion of normal factors. The investigator often only learns of a case weeks, months, or years after it has happened when memories have been perhaps eroded or distorted. Although many spontaneous cases are buttressed by excellent contemporary documentation, critics can attack many of them for one or another weakness of witnessing, recording, or reporting.

Laboratory experiments have provided better conditions for excluding alternative explanations. A wide variety of experiments has provided abundant and quite strong evidence of precognition. The first substantial experimental evidence for precognition came from the work of Carington, who used drawings as targets and a procedure for independent judging of the correspondence between the targets and the drawings made by the percipients. New drawings were placed in the target position (in Carington's study) each experimental day. It was found that the percipients tended to draw not only the target for a particular day but also the target for one or two days before and after that particular day (4). The results suggesting precognition in these investigations may possibly have derived from the use of contemporary extrasensory perception by the judges who matched the targets and drawings, so that they cannot be regarded as conclusive evidence for precognition.

Perhaps the best evidence for precognition derives from the experiments of Soal (38). In his first card-guessing experiments Soal did not initially expect or find evidence of precognition, but when he was advised (by Carington) to look for it anyway, he did so and discovered that two of his subjects had tended to guess one card ahead of the current target card in the experiments with a highly significant frequency. Soal then recalled these two subjects and tested them again. One (Stewart) then showed a significantly high score for the target card, but the other (Shackleton) still manifested the tendency to identify with significant frequency the card ahead of the target card and, under some conditions, the card two ahead of the current target. In some of Soal's experiments the target was selected and known in advance of the percipient's calls. But in other series, the target was selected by one of the experimenters who drew a single counter out of a bag or bowl containing two hundred thoroughly mixed counters of the same make and size but of five different colors. Each color corresponded to one of the five targets the agent would look at while the percipient made his call. A new counter was selected just before each trial so that up until that moment the target itself was not known or selected. In these experiments then Shackleton was cognizing a card that had not been selected at the time of his call.

A counter-explanation to precognition in the above experiments was that the selection of counters had been influenced by the selector's ESP to correspond with the call Shackleton had just made. Other experiments designed to test for precognition have raised similar questions about interpretations. It has been suggested that ESP might have been used to influence the shuffling of cards whose order was later to correspond with calls made by a percipient. Mechanical shuffling reduced, but did not eliminate, the possibility that such precognition experiments might really be demonstrating only psychokinesis, that is, the influence of mental impulses on physical objects, in these cases, the cards. Some ingenious methods were devised to eliminate interpretations other than precognition. For example, cuts of the cards were governed by numbers derived from temperature reports surely beyond the influence of ordinary human control (27). In other experiments figures taken from thrown dice were used to begin an arithmetical manipulation from which emerged the figures guiding the entry into a table of random numbers from which the targets were directly derived (18). This procedure was also thought beyond human influence and probably was.

I shall not take time to provide details of the many other laboratory investigations providing evidence of precognition. Suffice it to say that many parapsychologists believe that the occurrence of precognitions in the sense defined earlier has been amply demonstrated both in spontaneous cases and in laboratory experiments. For these parapsychologists, then, a problem exists—that of somehow explaining how some persons can seemingly become aware of events that have not yet happened.

PRECOGNITION AND DETERMINISM

Before considering explanatory theories for precognition, I wish to discuss briefly the bearing of the evidence for precognition on the question of determinism. It has been suggested that the evidence for precognition supports the concept of a rigid determinism governing events. This assumption is unjustified. Precognition and determinism are quite separate questions. If we observe an event in a separate portion of space, we do not believe that it was determined merely because we saw it happen. Similarly, we should not believe that an event is determined if we happen to see a facsimile of the event before it has happened (21).

It may possibly be true, however, that events which are pre-cognized *exactly* are determined (33). In other words, a require-ment for a completely accurate precognition may be that the pre-cognized event be determined. (This, even if true, would tell us nothing about determination of all other events.) Apart from this possibility, however, many cases have been reported in which the precognizing subject (or some other person) seems to have averted the exact "fulfillment" of the events foreseen, often as an apparent consequence of the experience that was taken as a warning. For ex-ample, in one nineteenth century case a woman dreamed that her coachman had fallen off the coach and struck his head on the pave-ment. She vividly saw his hat crushed as his head struck the ground. The next day her coachman fainted and started to fall off the coach, but the dreamer, remembering her dream, jumped from the coach just in time and called a nearby policeman to help; the latter caught the falling man before he struck his head (22, p. 497). In another instance a woman had a vision (when falling asleep) of an accident to a carriage she was to ride in and she got out of the carriage (when she remembered her dream) just in time to avoid being badly hurt in the immediately ensuing accident that corresponded with her dream (37, pp. 313-14). It may be said—correctly, I think—that in such cases the percipient does not precognize exactly events of the future but only foresees certain possible developments with various options available. Still it may be more accurate to say that certain events are correctly precognized and that to these the percipient (in his dream, vision, or other apparently paranormal experience) adds from inference other details which are not precognized and not "fulfilled" in the later events.

In some other cases, it should be added, the percipient tries might-ily to avoid the events he seems to foresee and fails (5, 29). A particularly impressive case of this type occurred in the death of Robert Morris, Sr., the father of the financier of the American Revolution. Having dreamed that he would be killed by the firing of a cannon from a ship he was to visit, he tried to avoid going on board the ship. His grounds for such reluctance seemed so absurd that he was eventually persuaded by the captain that it was entirely safe to board the ship as no guns would be fired until after he left. At the end of his visit, the captain ordered that a saluting gun should be fired only after he raised his hand when the party, including Robert Morris, had safely reached the shore. But as the captain's boat was still within range of the gun a fly lighted on his nose, and he raised his hand to brush it off. This was taken by the ship's gunner as the signal to fire and a fragment of the discharge hit Robert Morris and wounded him fatally (49, pp. 5-7). Even in cases of this type, however, we do not need to see anything inevitable in the events following the dream. We can believe that it was still open to Robert Morris to refuse to go on the ship, as indeed he at first tried to do. Many persons who have precognitive dreams or waking impressions disregard the warnings they contain and proceed to act in a manner that links their own lives with the fulfilling events. In a well-known case, a man who had booked passage on the *Titanic* dreamed twice that this ship was floating keel upwards with her passengers and crew swimming about her (19). Yet he did not cancel his ticket until after a change of business plans seemed to justify his doing so on rational grounds. Precognitions may in fact derive their accuracy from the inflexibility of many human beings. A psychological study of precognition subjects is needed to learn whether the persons involved in precognized events are less flexible—more predictable we might say—than other persons.

THEORIES OF PRECOGNITION

Parapsychologists dispose of numerous theories for explaining precognition, but only a few of them have gained general respect. Some theories of precognition involve strange concepts of time and causation and while their strangeness does not make them untrue, it has perhaps prevented their general acceptance. The fact that several different theories persist today indicates that we have no explanation judged completely satisfactory by all students of the subject. From the beginnings of modern investigations of precognition, numerous authors have contributed valuable (if often disagreeing) contributions to the theory of the topic (3, 8, 20, 30, 34, 47). Instead of attempting a review of all the different theories, I shall simply indicate some of the lines on which parapsychologists are working towards a solution of the problem of precognition.

It is sometimes thought that in ostensible precognition an event that has not yet occurred has somehow caused an event in the present, i.e. the precognizing experience. This seems to contradict our habitual concepts of causation and/or of time. Yet in fact no assumption of this kind is needed or sensible. I agree with Broad (3) that an event of the future has no existence and cannot cause anything. The ostensible precognizing experience is of something in the present. It can at best be an image (an imagination, if you prefer) of how an event that has not yet happened may occur in the future. We need to try to understand how it is that the images seen by the percipient in his present correspond so closely and often in small details with events that occur later.

It is possible that the subject, by paranormal means, gains access to information from which, once it is available to him, he can infer the future course of events. The sum of his inferences is then projected in the form of visual or other images which he relates to the future. An explanation of this kind may well apply to those numerous recorded instances in which a person who is totally unfamiliar with horses and betting has nevertheless dreamed of the winner of a horse race (17). Other persons have been down at the stables talking to the jockeys, looking at the horses, and in other ways normally assembling information on which they have based a conscious selection of the winner. The precognizing subject differs from these persons not in his powers of inference but in his powers of access to information. Instead of going to the stables he sleeps and the winner's name comes to his consciousness.

This type of explanation may account also for certain cases in which the percipient correctly foresees events in his own physical health. For example, a friend of mine who was pregnant had a vivid dream of details of her forthcoming delivery. These included that her baby would be born without anesthesia and would be stillborn. Since my friend was a diabetic, plans had already been made for delivery by caesarean section with an anesthetic. However, she went into labor prematurely and in a remote district of an Indian reservation. She was delivered naturally of the baby without anesthesia and the baby was stillborn. The percipient's husband corroborated for me both the telling of the dream during the pregnancy, when its fulfillment seemed most unlikely, and the subsequent events. In this case, one might suppose that the dreamer had a subconscious knowledge of the abnormal development of her pregnancy and its probable outcome prematurely and in a remote place without adequate medical facilities. She then presented the information to herself in the visual imagery of a vivid dream.

With regard to personal events lying in the future, it may be said that these events are nevertheless adumbrated in the events and decisions of the person affected earlier in his life. One requires only a higher (or deeper) view of a person, so to speak, in order to see what will happen to him in the future. An analogy here would be the situation of a man paddling a canoe in a river with steep embankments. Around the corner of the river beyond his sight and hearing lie dangerous rapids. Another man watching from the heights above can see both the man in the canoe and the rapids he will soon reach if he continues in his present course. Insights of this kind then are sometimes obtained by a person about himself or about other people.

If it is asked where the information about the future course of a man's life resides, the answer could be that it exists in some form in his subconscious mind. Just as in a person's body there may exist an invisible genetic program for his later death from, say, cancer, so his subconscious mind may, according to this theory, contain plans and indications of his future life. Sometimes the curtain separating conscious and subconscious aspects of the mind becomes pulled apart and a man glimpses details of his life plan not previously apparent, and some persons may glimpse details of other persons' futures in a similar way.

Precognitions of some events, especially certain disasters such as earthquakes and avalanches, require the acquisition of information known to no living person, even subconsciously. It must then be supposed that the subject acquires his information by clairvoyance (that is, without a living person as its source) instead of by telepathy in which a living person acts as agent.

The theory that I have outlined, that is, a combination of extrasensory perception and normal inference, is not so much a theory of precognition (defined earlier as noninferential knowledge of the future) as an alternative explanation applicable to many cases of ostensible precognition. There are two types of experiences that cannot be readily explained by this theory. They may be examples of true precognition. The first type of experience is that of spontaneous cases with a foretelling of the future many years in advance; in a later section I shall cite two examples of this. Secondly, true precognition may occur in certain experiments, in which complicated methods far beyond ordinary human knowledge or control are used to enter random number tables for the selection of targets. I have earlier given examples of such experiments (18, 27). In both these types of experiences it is difficult to see how anyone, even with very extended powers of contemporaneous extrasensory perception and inference, could possibly foretell the future in detail as seems to occur in some examples of such experiences and experiments. Thus true precognition may occur and may require some of the more recondite explanations that upset our habitual notions of cause and time.

I have already mentioned that psychokinesis has been proposed as a possible explanation for some experiments in precognition. It has also been evoked as an explanation for spontaneous cases of precognition. As I shall describe shortly, a large proportion of precognitions have as their themes deaths or serious accidents and illnesses. Some theorists have suggested that this indicates the effects of malevolent impulses on the part of the percipient. They suggest that the percipient wishes the death of another person. This death then becomes the theme of the apparent precognition. The death wish supposedly has the double effect of bringing into consciousness an image of the person's death (the precognition) and, through psychokinesis, of contributing to the death. This theory, first enunciated by Tanagras (45) has found favor with Roll (31) and Eisenbud (10, 11), but I think most parapsychologists feel that it is an unnecessary addition to the theory of precognition and one for which there is little empirical support. I am not denying that human beings may have adverse effects on each other in paranormal ways, only that this possibility does not seem a necessary factor in precognitions and I do not know of any strong evidence that it is.

Assuming that some paranormal explanation is called for to account for authentic cases of apparent precognition, a most important question is why certain persons have such experiences and others do not. Some hints of answers to this and related questions are found in an analysis of characteristics of several large series of precognitive experiences to which I shall turn next.

CHARACTERISTICS OF SPONTANEOUS PRECOGNITIVE EXPERIENCES

Several large series of spontaneous precognitions have been independently collected and analyzed. The cases derive from several different cultures of America, Europe, and Asia. The cases in these different series show remarkably similar characteristics, an observation which for me strengthens the evidence of precognition. At least it suggests that the reports of the cases are describing a natural and widespread human experience.

Frequency of Spontaneous Precognitive Experiences

We have no reliable information about the frequency of precognitive experiences in the general population. However, several large series of spontaneous cases of different kinds provide information about the frequency of precognitions within these series. Thus Sannwald found precognitions accounting for 52 per cent of one thousand German spontaneous cases (35). They were 34 per cent of three hundred English cases analyzed by Green (12). They were 40 per cent of 3,290 American cases analyzed by L. E. Rhine (28). All these series derived from reports voluntarily sent in (usually by the percipients themselves) to parapsychological institutes or societies. A survey in northern India required 2494 schoolchildren to answer a questionnaire on experiences suggestive of extrasensory perception, including precognitions. Of these children 36 per cent said they had had such experiences and 40 per cent of those responding affirmatively said they had had precognitive experiences (26). Whatever the actual incidence of ostensible precognitions, it is certain that among persons reporting experiences that are for them indicative of extrasensory perception a large number believes that their experiences refer to future events.

State of Consciousness of the Percipient

It was noted early in the S.P.R. studies of precognitions that these experiences tended to occur more often when the subject was asleep and dreaming than when he was awake. Thus in the 1888 series, 66 per cent of precognitions occurred during dreaming (37), in the 1934 series 68.1 per cent† were reported to occur during dreaming (34), and in the 1957 series 68.8 per cent were reported as occurring during dreaming (12).‡ Very similar figures were found in the American series in which 68 per cent occurred during dreaming (28) and in the German series in which 60 per cent occurred during dreaming. (35). The Indian series was an exception to this trend in that precognitive experiences occurred about equally during dreaming and in the waking state (26). For the other series, however, precognitions contrast sharply with contemporaneous ESP experiences, which tend to occur as often in the waking state as during dreaming. L. E. Rhine has suggested that attitudes prevalent in Western cultures make it easier for us to experience contemporaneous extrasensory perception than precognitions which seem to upset our usual concepts of time. Precognitive experiences therefore rise into consciousness more at night when barriers between conscious and unconscious portions of the mind are weaker (28). If this is so, then the Indian series may fail to show a difference in conditions required for precognitive and contemporaneous experiences because all extrasensory perceptions are, it is generally agreed, more acceptable and less inhibited in the Indian culture than in the West.

Sensory and Emotional Qualities of the Perception

In all kinds of extrasensory experiences occurring during dreams the percipients frequently comment on the fact that the dreams in which these experiences occur differ from their ordinary dreams. They often use the words "vivid" or "realistic" to distinguish such dreams from their usual dreams. These words actually are not quite synonymous. "Vivid" refers to the quality of sensory intensity and "realistic" to the quality of coherence and resemblance to our waking perceptions as opposed to the rapid changes of imagery that oc-

---

†A small number of cases is included in both of these first two S.P.R. series. So the derived figures for the per cent of the cases occurring during dreaming are not fully independent.

‡For these last two percentages I have adopted the adjusted calculations of Nicol (24).

cur in most dreams. Some percipients use both descriptive words in referring to dreams that seem to have an element of extrasensory perception in them. In a series of 125 precognitive dreams§ that I analyzed, the percipients characterized 45 per cent of them as "vivid" or "realistic" or they used some similar adjective. Although not all vivid dreams have a component of extrasensory perception, and not all precognitive dreams are vivid, the quality of vividness seems an excellent indicator of extrasensory perception, including precognition.

Many precognitive dreams occur two or more times with little or no variation. Such recurrence was reported in 14 per cent of the 125 miscellaneous precognitive dreams I have analyzed.

A great many of these experiences carry conviction to the dreamer that he is in fact seeing a portion of the future. Whether such conviction derives from the sensory qualities, the recurrence of the dream (when this happens), or from other factors such as emotional accompaniments of the experience, we cannot easily tell and no doubt the significant factor promoting conviction varies from one percipient to another. One test of conviction is that the percipient takes some action in an effort to avert the future event if it seems unfavorable, and a considerable number of the percipients do take such averting action. Of the 125 percipients of the precognitive dreams I have analyzed, thirty-four (27%) tried to avert fulfillment of the precognized events. The proportion would be much higher if we considered only those cases in which the dreamer would want to avert fulfillment since about a third of the dreams of this series related to trivial, unimportant, or favorable events the dreamer would not have disliked or would have welcomed. L. E. Rhine separated out 433 precognitive dreams concerned with events that the persons involved would ordinarily wish to avoid, and she found that in 162 (37%) of them the dreamer had attempted to avert fulfillment. (29). In another much smaller series of precogni-

§This series of 125 apparently precognitive dreams is a miscellaneous collection, not one collected systematically. The cases in the series are of uneven authenticity, some being well documented and investigated, others not. I believe, however, that it is justified to use the series as a pilot study preliminary to a full-scale investigation of the characteristics of large numbers of cases. This series contains no case included in any other series referred to in this paper.

tive dreams, 80 per cent were characterized as having an "insistent, compelling character" (17).

Symbolism in the Experience

Symbols do not occur prominently in identified precognitive experiences. They were reported in 13.5 per cent of the 125 miscellaneous precognitive dreams I analyzed and in 5 to 6 per cent of the S.P.R. cases (of precognitive dreams) analyzed by Saltmarsh (34). On the other hand, some precognitive dreamers have reported identifying symbols that are, for them, reliable indicators of future events (9, 48). If more such dreamers could be identified, the yield of veridical precognitive dreams could be raised. It is important for the dreamer (or recorder) to indicate the meaning of symbols or associations *before* the related events have occurred. Failure to do this leaves open the possibility of retrospective assignment of more successes than the facts justify.

Relationship of Percipient and Agent

In contemporaneous spontaneous cases indicative of extrasensory perception, the percipient and agent have, in the majority of cases, a close personal relationship. They are usually members of the same biological or marital family. Although some of this preponderance of family relationships between percipients and agents may derive from artifacts in the collection of cases, there are grounds, which I have discussed elsewhere (43), for thinking that such errors would not affect the findings significantly.

In precognitive experiences the dream or other impressions often have to do with a future event in which the percipient himself will participate, although other persons may be included in the experience and in the related and apparently fulfilling events. Thus in the 125 precognitive dreams I analyzed, the percipient dreamed of some event happening to himself in 61 (49%) of the cases. In the Indian series the percipient had a precognitive experience about himself in 18 per cent of the cases. (In some such cases the experience included other persons in addition to the dreamer himself.) When, however, the percipient precognizes some event in the future life of another person, that other person is, as with contemporaneous experiences, much more often a close relative than otherwise. For example, close relatives were dreamed about in 31 per cent of the 125 precognitive dreams I analyzed, distant relatives, friends and acquaintances in 11 per cent, and strangers in 9 per cent. In the Indian series the agents and percipients were members of the same families in 59 per cent of the cases with female percipients and in 41.4 per cent of the cases with male percipients. Similar proportions are suggested in the data of the German series, although in Sannwald's reports of that series contemporaneous and precognitive experiences are not analyzed separately with regard to this feature (35, 36).

It might seem to follow from this that precognition is rarely experienced in regard to events happening outside one's immediate family circle. This is in general true, but there are some odd exceptions to this trend found in the data of the experiences related to the sinking of the *Titanic* and the Aberfan coal-tip disaster, in both of which relatively few of the percipients had any connection with persons actually involved in the disaster. Also a disaster in France during an automobile race in which seventy persons were killed seems to have been accurately precognized by a woman in Italy (48).

Themes of the Experiences

The themes of precognitive experiences (as of most other spontaneous ESP experiences) are mostly serious and shocking events such as deaths, accidents, and grave illnesses. Comparatively few of these experiences have as their themes a trivial or pleasant event. Death is the commonest single event related to precognitive experiences. The following table summarizes the related events in precognitive experiences of three different series.

TABLE 1

RELATED EVENTS IN PRECOGNITIVE EXPERIENCES IN THREE SERIES

(percentages only)

	S.P.R. Series 1934		Miscellaneous European and American Series		Indian Schoolchildren Series
Death	35		47		27*
Violent		9.4		33.5	
Natural		25.6		13.5	
Accidents	20		17		24
Illnesses	6		4		7
All other events	39		32		42

*Breakdowns of data into violent and natural deaths not given in the report of this series.

Of importance, I think, is the fact that illnesses are the related events in such experiences less often than accidents. This accords with a suggestion I shall return to later; namely, that an emotional shock is a factor tending to generate precognitive experiences and, for that matter, other types of extrasensory perceptions. Accidents, being almost by definition unexpected, are likely to generate more shock than illnesses. The importance of shock is further suggested by the fact that in the series of 125 precognitive dreams I analyzed many more of the deaths were violent than natural and they were therefore usually quite unexpected. (The 1934 S.P.R. series did not, however, show a preponderance of violent over natural deaths in the themes of the precognitions.) The preponderance of violent deaths in the series of 125 precognitive dreams is not due to war since only one of the deaths was directly related to military action. On the other hand, one might expect that war with its increased numbers of accidents and violent deaths would provide occasions for more numerous precognitions. As already mentioned, Sannwald found in a German series of spontaneous cases that precognitive experiences were more numerous (52%) than contemporaneous experiences (48%). (35). This proportion of precognitions far exceeds the proportions of precognitions in the other series, mentioned earlier. The experiences of the German series occurred during wartime, whereas those of the other series occurred more (although not exclusively) during periods of peace.

Errors of sampling may account for some bias towards death and serious misfortunes as the reported themes of precognitive experiences since percipients may have a greater tendency to remember such events than others having less emotional intensity. It is doubtful, however, if this can account for all the preponderance of such misfortunes as death in the themes of the experiences, because favorable events associated with joy, such as births, weddings, and so forth, should be remembered equally well and yet they figure relatively infrequently in precognitive experiences and also in contemporaneous experiences suggestive of extrasensory perception.

Another odd feature of the data is that percipients very rarely seem to precognize some hostile attack on themselves by other persons, although there are rare exceptions such as President Lincoln's well-known dream of his own assassination a few weeks before this happened (16).

Time Interval Between Precognition and Related Events

The interval between the subject's experience and the related event is usually short; that is, a few days or hours only. In a Dutch series of 193 apparently precognitive dreams, the great majority occurred within twenty-four hours of the related events (14), and this has been observed in other series. In cases of major disasters with multiple percipients, the precognitive experiences increase in frequency as the time of the disaster approaches. Thus four of the ten precognitions of the *Titanic* that I studied occurred within ten days of her sinking, the other six being scattered over periods farther back from the disaster (39, 42). In the Aberfan coal-tip disaster eighteen of thirty-four precognitions occurred within four days of the disaster, another eight within two weeks of it, and the remaining eight were scattered irregularly over the preceding weeks and months(1).

This piling up of precognitive experiences as the related events come nearer is, I think, harmonious with the suggestion I made earlier, namely, that the percipient subconsciously makes normal inferences from paranormally derived information. Presumably as an event comes nearer to actualization the causal processes that will bring it about become less subject to modification. The event becomes more inevitable, we could say. At the same time, more persons may have access, even subconsciously, to data relating to the causes which, if they were to become known, would provide a basis for inferences about the event to come. There is nothing different in this from what we are used to in our normal observations of ourselves and others. At a remote time from some future event, such as a journey, plans about it are loose and readily changed; as the event comes nearer the plans become hardened and we and others can predict more accurately the details of what we shall actually do when the day for the event, say a departure, arrives.

As I mentioned earlier, however, occasionally quite detailed precognitions occur several or many years before the related events. A well-known example in the British literature occurred in a dream experienced by the percipient three times during a six-year period

before the death of her uncle. The details, which all turned out to be correct, included the location of the dead man's body on a path, his horse nearby, and the unusual item that when the body was being carried upstairs in the house after it was brought in, the left hand hung down and struck the banister (22, pp. 334-593). In a dream reported by Bender the percipient seemed to foresee rather unusual details of a death that occurred twenty-seven years later. The dream occurred when the "agent" was a mere infant two weeks old (2). Authentic cases of this kind, and there are a number of them, do not fit easily into the hypothesis of contemporary extrasensory perception with normal (subconscious) inference that I favor as explaining most instances of ostensible precognition.

THE SENSITIVITY OF INDIVIDUAL PERSONS TO CERTAIN THEMES

When a person has an apparently paranormal perception of some event distant in space or time, one is interested in knowing why he happened to perceive this particular event. As I have already indicated, a partial answer to this question is provided by the frequent close personal relationship that the percipient usually has with the persons figuring in the perception and related events. However, some persons dream of events happening to strangers and one still needs to ask why they dreamed of these particular events. The data available contain hints, although not much more, that persons tend to dream about events that have particular significance for them. Thus in one case I studied (not precognitive but postcognitive in this case), the dreamer had, I am satisfied, an extrasensory awareness of a distant airplane crash. He had a lifelong interest in airplanes and had wished to be a pilot himself (41). In another case, the dreamer precognized a fire on a particular ship. On investigation she was found to have had extensive connections with ships (13). This topic and the evidence for it has been particularly investigated by Tenhaeff in the Netherlands (46). He has studied these "specializations" of percipients with regard to contemporaneous extrasensory perception, but as I have said, there is a little evidence suggesting that the same tendency occurs in precognition. There is nothing surprising in these observations when we remember that we tend to dream of *past* events of special significance to us. We should expect our dreams of the future to be similarly influenced by our interests and special concerns.

If we consider the characteristics of precognitive experiences mentioned in the foregoing section, we can easily assign to precognition an adaptive function in our lives. The majority of them have to do with serious or fatal misfortunes and are related to the percipient himself or persons emotionally close to him. In short, precognition seems to occur in just those situations where our emotions are most strongly aroused—threats to the well-being of ourselves and those we love. As I have already mentioned, however, in some precognitions the percipient becomes aware of some calamity quite remote from his personal affairs. This brings me finally to the precognition of disasters with multiple fatalities and more than one percipient.

PRECOGNITIONS OF DISASTERS WITH MULTIPLE FATALITIES

Unfortunately there have been few investigations of precognitions of disasters involving more than one killed or injured person and more than one percipient. I shall refer to only three such investigations.

Cox investigated twenty-eight serious railroad accidents in the United States with ten or more injuries of persons. (6). He obtained counts of the numbers of passengers aboard the trains on the days of the accidents and on the seven days preceding the accident and on the days two, three, and four weeks before the accidents. He showed that the numbers of passengers were significantly smaller on the days of the accidents as compared with preceding days of the same train runs. He found the effect greater for coach than for Pullman passengers. Cox interpreted his data as indicating that many passengers had a subliminal precognitive impression of the impending accident and (without being aware of why they did so) changed their plans so that they did not travel on that train. The greater effect on coach than on Pullman passengers may be explained in the following way. Pullman passengers reserve their space usually several days in advance, are usually traveling farther than coach passengers, and are less likely to cancel their plans and reservations for seemingly superficial reasons.

The second investigation I wish to mention is one that I made myself in collecting and analyzing nineteen apparently paranormal experiences related to the sinking of the *Titanic* in 1912 (39, 42). Some of these experiences were only first recorded long after the event, but others were reported or recorded before or soon after the disaster and altogether I was able to assemble a considerable amount of corroborated reports suggesting that these nineteen percipients had had extrasensory awareness of the sinking of the *Titanic*. Ten of the cases were precognitive.

Of interest in connection with the sinking of the *Titanic* was why there seemed to be so many more reported paranormal experiences connected with it than with other marine disasters of comparable magnitude such as, for example, the equally disastrous sinking by a German submarine of the Cunard steamer *Lusitania* in 1915. (The loss of life from the sinking of the *Lusitania* was not much less than that from the sinking of the *Titanic*.) I could find only a very few reports of claimed paranormal experiences related to the sinking of the *Lusitania*. Also one could ask, Why are not many other disasters, such as battles, associated more often with reported precognitions? A tentative answer I gave to this question is that the sinking of the *Titanic* was totally unexpected. At the time of her maiden, and only voyage, she was considered unsinkable, incredible as that now seems. Her double hull, allegedly watertight bulkheads, and other features were really thought to have rendered her unsinkable and an almost arrogant conviction of this led Captain Smith to ignore the warnings about icebergs that he received so that he permitted his ship to steam at full speed through an area of the north Atlantic abounding with icebergs. There was thus a severe shock to crew and passengers alike when the *Titanic*, after striking an iceberg, was found to be sinking. The hardened conviction of many of them that the ship was unsinkable undoubtedly contributed to the loss of life since many passengers refused to enter the lifeboats which could have saved them. In contrast, the sinking of the *Lusitania* was normally predictable. The Germans had declared unrestricted submarine warfare against all shipping going to the Allies in Europe. They hinted strongly in advertisements in New York newspapers that they would sink the *Lusitania*. No one can have sailed on her without doubting if he would reach Great Britain alive. I suggest that the very unexpectedness of the sinking of the *Titanic* may have generated an emotional shock not present in disasters that are less surprising such as the sinking of the *Lusitania* and most military battles. The shock may have contributed to the production of the relatively large number of paranormal experiences related to the *Titanic*.

The third investigation is of a much more recent disaster. On October 21, 1966, a massive coal-tip slid down a mountainside and engulfed the Welsh mining village of Aberfan, killing 144 persons, mostly children attending a school in the path of the landslide. An English psychiatrist, J. C. Barker, who had some interest in premonitions, arranged for an appeal through a national newspaper to persons who believed they had had some foreknowledge of the disaster (1). Such persons were asked to send in reports of their experiences and supporting corroborations if available. The appeal was launched a week after the disaster. Barker received seventy-six letters in reply and when the cases were probed further and vague or inadequately documented ones were set aside, he found he still had thirty-five cases in which the percipient's account seemed worthy of confidence. The percipients were scattered over England and Wales. In twenty-four cases Barker obtained corroboration that the percipient had spoken of his experience before the disaster at Aberfan had occurred. The accounts varied widely in details and in the correspondence of their details with the facts of the disaster, but I think, judging from the short summaries Barker published, that most persons would agree that these experiences (25 out of the 35 were dreams) had a relationship to the Aberfan disaster. However, since many of the details were lacking in specificity, I am not sure that these experiences would have been thought to point towards the Aberfan disaster *before* it happened, especially if they had been studied separately instead of together. Yet taken as a group, and considering their close temporal connection with the disaster itself, it is difficult to avoid the impression that there was a connection between the disaster and at least many of these experiences.

The several recent political assassinations in this country have been followed by numerous claims from persons who say that they had some foreknowledge of them. However, few of these prophets seem to have recorded their predictions in writing before the events.‖ I do know, however, of two corroborated predictions of the assassination of Senator Robert F. Kennedy on June 5, 1968.

In the first case the percipient had several dreams that he thought pointed to the assassination of Senator Kennedy in the near future. He wrote a short description of his dreams and their interpretation and sent these to two parapsychologists about a week and a month respectively before June 5th. The dream imagery contained some details that corresponded with details of the actual shooting of Senator Kennedy, although others did not.

In the second case, the percipient had a dream of Mrs. Robert Kennedy dressed in widow's black coming down the steps of a large building followed by all her children. She had this dream one or two days (she did not remember exactly which) before Senator Kennedy's assassination and told it before this event to a friend who corroborated to me that she had done so.

Parapsychologists wish that more such predictions could be recorded in writing before the related events actually happen.¶ The large number of claims made afterwards about the predictions of such murders and the large number of generally corroborated claims of prediction made in connection with the Aberfan disaster have stimulated interest among parapsychologists in a systematic gathering of premonitions. As a result two central premonitions bureaus have been set up in London and New York.** These bureaus receive reports of ostensible precognitions sent in by percipients before the related events have happened. The bureaus will analyze the reports and search for common themes or persons mentioned or suggested in them. The detection of

‖Political assassinations are not the best topic for assessing the accuracy of precognition. First, politically prominent persons are at high risk for assassination, and secondly they are ordinarily much more thought about and dreamed about by many persons than are other strangers to the dreamers. There is thus a much greater likelihood of a chance correlation between a dream of a political figure and his murder or sudden death in another way.

¶Persons willing to record precognitive impressions in advance of the related events are invited to communicate with the Secretary, Division of Parapsychology, Department of Psychiatry, University of Virginia School of Medicine, Charlottesville, Virginia 22901, U.S.A.

**See next page for footnote.*

such common themes may lead to better documentation of the occurrence of precognitions recorded before the related events. At a later stage, it may be possible to use the premonitions sent in to the bureaus like a distant early warning system, alerting persons or communities threatened with some disaster so that they may take precautionary measures to avert it.

The possibility of such an application of paranormal powers may seem a distant goal to reach, but the evidence for precognition so far obtained seems fully to justify further investigations of the kinds of experiences that have provided much of this evidence.

**Following are the addresses of these premonitions bureaus:
1. British Premonitions Bureau
   Grove House
   14 West Grove
   London, S.E. 10, England
2. Central Premonitions Registry
   Box 482, Times Square Station
   New York, N. Y. 10036.

Percipients may send their dreams to both the Division of Parapsychology, Department of Psychiatry, University of Virginia School of Medicine, and one of the premonitions bureaus if they wish.

REFERENCES

1. BARKER, J.C.: Premonitions of the Aberfan disaster. *J S.P.R.*, *44*:169-181, 1967.
2. BENDER, H.: Previsions of disaster. In Garrett, Eileen J. (Ed.): *Beyond the Five Senses.* New York, J. B. Lippincott, 1957.
3. BROAD, C.D.: The notion of "Precognition." In Smythies, J. (Ed.): *Science and ESP.* London, Routledge and Kegan Paul, 1967.
4. CARINGTON, W.: Experiments on the paranormal cognition of drawings. *Proc S.P.R.*, *46*:34-151; 277-344, 1940-41.
5. COX, W.E.: Precognition: An analysis. I. *J A.S.P.R.*, *50*:47-58, 1956.
6. COX, W.E.: Precognition: An analysis. II. *J A.S.P.R.*, *50*:99-109, 1956.
7. DALE, L.A.; WHITE, R., and MURPHY, G.: A selection of cases from a recent survey of spontaneous ESP phenomena. *J A.S.P.R.*, *56*:3-47, 1962.
8. DOBBS, H.A.C.: Time and extrasensory perception. *Proc S.P.R.*, *54*:249-361, 1965.
9. DOMMEYER, F.C.: Some ostensibly precognitive dreams. *J A.S.P.R.*, *49*:108-117, 1955.
10. EISENBUD, J.: Precognition, anxiety and aggression. *J Parapsychol*, *19*:111-114, 1955.

11. EISENBUD, J.: Compound theories of precognition. *J S.P.R.*, *41*:353-355, 1962.
12. GREEN, C.: Analysis of spontaneous cases. *Proc S.P.R.*, *53*:97-161, 1960.
13. HEYWOOD, R., and STEVENSON, I.: The connections between previous experiences and an apparently precognitive dream. *J A.S.P.R.*, *60*:32-45, 1966.
14. KOOY, J.M.J.: Cited by W.H.C. Tenhaeff in *Hellsehen und Telepathie*. German edition of *Telepathie en Helderziendheid*. Gutersloh, C. Bertelsmann Verlag, 1962.
15. LAMBERT, G.W.: A precognitive dream about a waterspout. *J S.P.R.*, *43*:5-10, 1965.
16. LAMON, W.H.: *Recollections of Abraham Lincoln. 1847-1865*. Chicago, A.C. McClurg and Co., 1895.
17. LYTTELTON, E.: *Some Cases of Prediction*. London, G. Bell and Sons, Ltd., 1937.
18. MANGAN, G.L.: Evidence of displacement in a precognition test. *J Parapsychol*, *19*:35-44, 1955.
19. MIDDLETON, J.C.: Correspondence. *J S.P.R.*, *15*:264-268, 1912.
20. MUNDLE, C.W.K.: Does the concept of precognition make sense? *Int J Parapsychol*, *6* (No. 2):179-94, 1964.
21. MURPHY, G.: An approach to precognition. *J A.S.P.R.*, *42*:3-14, 1948.
22. MYERS, F.W.H.: The subliminal self. *Proc S.P.R.*, *11*:334-593, 1895.
23. MYERS, F.W.H.: *Human Personality and Its Survival of Bodily Death*. London, Longmans, Green and Co., 1903, 2 vols.
24. NICOL, J.F.: Apparent spontaneous precognition: A historical review. *Int J Parapsychol*, *3* (No. 2): 26-39, 1961.
25. PAINE, A.B.: *Mark Twain: A Biography*. New York, Harper & Brothers, 1912.
26. PRASAD, J., and STEVENSON, I.: A survey of psychical experiences in school children of Uttar Pradesh. *Int J Parapsychol*, *10* (No. 3):241-261, 1968.
27. RHINE, J.B.: Evidence of precognition in the covariation of salience ratios. *J Parapsychol*, *6*:111-143, 1942.
28. RHINE, L.E.: Frequency of types of experiences in spontaneous precognition. *J Parapsychol*, *18*:92-123, 1954.
29. RHINE, L.E.: Precognition and intervention. *J Parapsychol*, *19*:1-34, 1955.
30. ROBERTSON, L.C.: The logical and scientific implications of precognition, assuming this to be established statistically from the work of card-guessing subjects. *J S.P.R.*, *39*:134-139, 1957.
31. ROLL, W.G.: The problem of precognition. *J S.P.R.*, *41*:115-128, 1961.
32. ROYCE, J.: Pseudo-presentiments. Part III of "Report of the Committee on Phantasms and Presentiments." *Proc A.S.P.R.*, *1*:366-392, 1889.
33. RYZL, M.: Precognition and intervention. *J Parapsychol*, *19*:192-197, 1957.

34. SALTMARSH, H.F.: Report on cases of apparent precognition. *Proc S.P.R.*, 42:49-98, 1934.
35. SANNWALD, G.: Statistische Untersuchungen an Spontanphänomenen. *Z Parapsychologie und Grenzgebiete der Psychologie*, 3:59-71, 1959.
36. SANNWALD, G.: Zur Psychologie Paranormaler Spontanphänomene: Motivation, Thematik und Bezugspersonen "okkulter" Erlebnisse. *Z Parapsychologie und Grenzgebiete der Psychologie*, 3:149-183, 1959.
37. SIDGWICK, E.M.: On the evidence for premonitions. *Proc S.P.R.*, 5:288-354, 1888-89.
38. SOAL, S.G., and BATEMAN, F.: *Modern Experiments in Telepathy*. London, Faber and Faber, Ltd., 1954.
39. STEVENSON, I.: A review and analysis of paranormal experiences connected with the sinking of the *Titanic*. *J A.S.P.R.*, 54:153-171, 1960.
40. STEVENSON, I: An example illustrating the criteria and characteristics of precognitive dreams. *J A.S.P.R.*, 55:98-103, 1961.
41. STEVENSON, I.: A postcognitive dream illustrating some aspects of the pictographic process. *J A.S.P.R.*, 57:182-202, 1963.
42. STEVENSON, I.: Seven more paranormal experiences associated with the sinking of the *Titanic*. *J A.S.P.R.*, 59:211-225, 1965.
43. STEVENSON, I.: Telepathic impressions. A review and report of thirty-five cases. *Proc A.S.P.R.* (In press).
44. STEVENSON, I.: The substantiality of spontaneous cases. Presidential Address, Eleventh Annual Convention of the Parapsychological Association, Freiburg, Germany, 1968. Proceedings of the Parapsychological Association, Vol. 5, (In press).
45. TANAGRAS, A.: *Le Destin et la Chance*. English translation published as *Psychophysical Elements in Parapsychological Traditions*. New York, Parapsychology Foundation, 1967.
46. TENHAEFF, W.H.C.: *Hellsehen und Telepathie*. (German translation of Telepathic en Helderzienheid.) Gutersloh, C. Bertelsmann Verlag, 1962.
47. THOULESS, R.H.: Experimental precognition and its implications. *J S.P.R.*, 35:201-210, 1950.
48. WEST, D.J.: Comments on a new approach to the study of paranormal dreams. *J S.P.R.*, 39:181-186, 1958.
49. YOUNG, E.: *Forgotten Patriot, Robert Morris*. New York, Macmillan, 1950.

Chapter 2

PSYCHOLOGICAL REACTIONS TO LIFE-THREATENING ILLNESS

ACUTE MYOCARDIAL INFARCTION

THOMAS P. HACKETT AND N. H. CASSEM

MY INTEREST in life-threatening illnesses had been largely confined to cancer patients until a day in the spring of 1958 when I first came across the monitor cardiac pacemaker. My office is on the third floor of the Bulfinch Building at the Massachusetts General Hospital. To reach it I have to walk through a large intensive-care ward. On this particular morning a familiar but unexpected sound caught my ear. It was the incessant, annoying peep of a newly-hatched chicken. As I remember, Easter had just passed and my first thought was that some foolish visitor had carried a chick in as a joke and allowed it to escape. I began a search and soon found that the source of the sound was, in fact, an electrodyne monitor cardiac pacemaker. I examined the machine, noting that the front panel contained an oscilloscope across which an ECG tracing constantly moved and a red light that blinked synchronously with the pulse and, of course, with the audible "bleep." It impressed me as a terrible contraption to be hooked up to.

I inquired about its function and learned that it monitored heart rate and provided an automatic electrical stimulus to the chest wall to prod the heart when it stopped or its rate dropped beneath a certain level. Loose leads could also trigger off the alarm and

Note: This study is from the Department of Psychiatry, Massachusetts General Hospital. Work performed under a contract (PHS-43-67-1443) with the National Institute of Health, Public Health Service, United States Department of Health, Education and Welfare.

did so far more frequently than cardiac arrest. The alarm, in those days, was a claxon, the sound of which galvanized the arrest team into action. It was perfectly possible for a drowsy patient to dislodge an electrode by turning over or shifting his weight, a mishap that would result in mayhem. Suddenly, his sleep would be shattered by a clanging bell and he would be jarred awake by a great jolt of electricity. Seconds later the bed would be surrounded by nurses and doctors ready to pound on his chest and open it, should that be necessary. More than once the pounding commenced before the team noticed that the patient was alert and quite well except for a loose lead.

With these facts in hand it did not take us long to work up a vigorous set of objections to this form of treatment. We thought it unnecessary to have the machine at the patient's bedside and heedlessly callous to have the "bleep" within earshot. When three or four of these noisemakers were going at the same time the resulting soundtrack made one think he had wandered into a heron rookery at dusk. We thought the noise along with the constant visual confrontation of the ECG plus the continuous threat of gratuitous shocking would serve to drive a large portion of the patient population into delirium or psychosis. Moreover, we predicted the instrument would frighten some people to death. Aside from the fact that the monitor cardiac pacemaker saved lives, we had nothing good to say about it. Nonetheless, the machine and the space it and the patient occupied furnished what seemed to be an ideal, almost laboratory setting in which to study life-death stress. The patients, for the most part, had just sustained a myocardial infarction and ran about a one in three chance of succumbing. The machinery, we fully believed, could do nothing but serve as a constant reminder to the patient of his peril. Thus with Olympian impartiality and dispassionate detachment we set out to prove that the cardiologists were so caught up by the gadget they had created to pace the heart that they had lost sight of the heart's owner.

Ivor Browne, my colleague in the research, and I then set out to interview and follow every patient who was attached to a monitor cardiac pacemaker in the intensive-care ward. In the course of twelve months we examined nineteen cases. The interviews, with the patients' consent, were taped. We introduced ourselves as physicians interested in how patients reacted to being monitored and asked for their help in answering a few questions. None refused. Depending upon the gravity of the patient's condition early interviews lasted from ten minutes to half an hour. We put our questions into the format of a standard medical history and review of systems so that very few suspected we were psychiatrists. The interview was designed to be as nonstressful as we could make it.

Of the nineteen patients, selected solely because they required the monitor cardiac pacemaker, fourteen were males, five females. They ranged in age from forty-six to eighty-two with a mean of 66 and a median of 68. They remained in the unit an average of 3.8 days and none died. Rather than being confined to one room they were scattered through various rooms on the critical care floor.

As the material began to accumulate we lost much of the initial confidence in our predictions! Although 26 per cent of the sample were confused and intermittently delirious as we had suspected, only one of the nineteen was frightened and complained spontaneously of being made nervous by the machine. The rest denied the presence of fear, apprehension or depression in relation both to the pacemaker and to their heart trouble. In other words, only a single patient behaved the way we predicted the lot of them would. It came as a surprise, one of the many we were to experience(1).

For the purpose of this study, we define "denial" as the conscious or unconscious repudiation of all or a portion of the total available meaning of an illness in order to allay anxiety and to minimize emotional stress (2). The eighteen patients we describe as using denial by no means presented this defense in identical ways. Some rationalized their fears, others avoided talking or thinking of their health while the remainder concentrated upon minor worries, such as hemorrhoids, in an attempt to exclude the more serious condition from consciousness. Despite the variety of methods employed to deny, two distinct patterns emerged, distinguished by the degree of rigidity with which the patient maintained this defence. The term "major denial" is used to describe those patients who stated unequivocally and unremittingly that they experienced no anxiety as a result of their illness or during their time on the monitor-pacemaker. Twelve major deniers (63%) were found in this sample. The term "partial denial" applies to those patients who initially denied being frightened by their illness or the machinery of survival but who eventually admitted concern. Six patients (32%) comprised the partial denier group.

There are characteristics particular to each group. The major denier demonstrates a lifelong pattern of minimizing danger and of underreacting to threatening situations. He rarely consults physicians for even the most serious of illnesses and is staunchly fatalistic. Throughout the course of his experience on the pacemaker he maintains a persistent indifference to his fate, denies experiencing the fear of dying, and disclaims ever having been afraid. All patients in this category were brought to the hospital unconscious or by others. No major deniers came spontaneously.

The cliche was a common method of renouncing danger. Typical of the major deniers' response was the following. We had asked a fifty-two-year-old longshoreman why the prospect of another cardiac arrest did not bother him. "Why worry? If the marker's got your name on it, you've got to buy it." Another, disclaiming any concern about being attached to a cardiac monitor, said, "Some people would be scared (by the machine) but not me. I'm called the 'iron man.' " A third, when asked how he could have gone through four days in the unit, including witnessing a fatal cardiac arrest, without having a thought or a care for death answered, "My middle name is Lucky." The following is a typical case history of a major denier.

> A sixty-three-year-old Jewish salesman entered the hospital in shock for an acute myocardial infarction. After recovering consciousness he maintained an air of friendly indifference to his disease. He was most cooperative in following orders and was well liked by his physicians but at no time did he express the least concern about his future. When questioned specifically he disclaimed any fear of the consequences of cardiac trouble because he was certain his heart was far better than the doctors let on. He also told us it was not his custom to worry, never had been. His wife corroborated this story. He reminisced about a World War I experience in which his vessel had been

torpedoed and he found himself alone floating on a piece of flotsam in the South Atlantic. Asked if that worried him he replied, "Why should it? After all, I was in one of the main shipping lanes and was bound to be picked up." Shipping lanes, as you know, are a hundred miles wide, not to mention storms and the other hazards of the sea.

The partial denier often gave the same initial impression as his major counterpart. He might begin by disclaiming all fear, but its presence was revealed in subsequent statements. For example, one patient began saying, "I wasn't afraid because if I'm gonna go, there is nothing I can do about it. When my number's called, I'm gonna go—why panic?" This was followed by, "you've got to be alarmed a little, but why go all to pieces." A major denier would not have acknowledged the presence of alarm. Typical of the partial denier is the following account.

An Irish matriarch of seventy-four was admitted for an episode of asystole which was followed by a myocardial infarction. When asked about the monitor pacemaker she at first thought it was "indeed a gorgeous piece of furniture, like a console television." As in speaking of her cardiac illness in general, she denied emphatically any fear. But then as the interview progressed and she remembered waking in the night and peering at the luminous tracing of the ECG she remarked, "Oh, I'd watch it flickerin' down and flarin' up, wonderin' withir it was pointing the way to heaven or hell for these old bones and it made me cold and shivery." Thus she gave us a vivid description of fear without exactly putting a name on it.

The one individual who feared the machine was a fifty-six-year-old Jewish laborer who was surprised to have come down with a coronary since his health was so good. Once attached to the monitor-cardiac pacemaker he became openly fearful and anxious. He said he could not bear to hear and watch the machine recording "every breath, every beat of my heart." Even though he realized it was there to help him he would have traded the safety it offered for being rid of it. He experienced obvious relief when the machine was removed.

In summary, what we learned in this study is that most people tend to deny the fear of death from serious illness and that they succeed, or at least they appear to succeed to a greater than lesser degree. Even the four patients who required painful external pacing to maintain their heartbeat did not evidence more anxiety than the others nor did they develop chronic anxiety neurosis.

When that study was concluded and written up we felt dissatisfied with the result. The series was small and the findings were provocative, but nothing more. We had learned a valuable personal lesson; namely, that it was foolish to expect the patient to feel and behave the way you imagined you would in his position. But there were more questions than answers. We wondered whether or not the major denier existed in the general population in the same percentage (63%) as we found him. Furthermore we questioned the value of denial, whether it protected the individual physiologically. For that matter we wondered if it effectively abetted the patient's psychological defence against fear. It was perfectly possible for them to be pretending fearlessness. We took what they told us at face value unless there were obvious discrepancies between affect and utterance. Although their responses were consistent and we cross-checked them with the closest relative, the internist, and at least one nurse involved in the case, aside from these, we had no objective measure to back up our impression.

Seven years went by during which time the technology of monitoring, pacing, and defibrillating advanced markedly and the concept of coronary care units developed. We continued to see coronary patients but in an unsystematic fashion. In 1967 a windfall came our way in the form of a contract from the National Institute of Health, Public Health Service, U. S. Department of Health, Education and Welfare. This enabled us to reevaluate our earlier work under better conditions and with far more patients. Dr. Ned Cassem joined me in this investigation and has been my co-worker ever since. Also in the team is another psychiatrist, Dr. Howard Wishnie, who is in charge of follow-up visits, usually in patient's home. We have a psychiatric social worker who interviews relatives and a polygrapher who records physiologic measurements from patients in the coronary care unit. A skilled psychiatric nurse holds group meetings with discharged patients. Recently, we have been able to add a biochemical facility for running catechole amines.

Our first task was to systematically investigate the experience of receiving intensive care in a coronary unit (3). Intensive care, per se, had been seriously indicated by a number of investigations as being partly responsible for the high psychiatric morbidity (30 to 70%) common to these units. We reasoned that if this were so, then some aspects of intensive care must be more responsible than others for the so-called intensive care syndrome (4, 5). We divided the experience up into components such as (1) reactions to the unit itself (size, wall color, quality of light, etc.); (2) reactions to being monitored; (3) predominant affects of patients; (4) reactions to witnessing cardiac arrest; (5) reaction to being given the Last Rites; (6) effect of surviving cardiac arrest; and (7) predominant defense mechanisms. There are more categories but we need not bring them up now. For this morning's discussion, I would like to limit my presentation to the seven areas just mentioned. Our interview method was the same as we used before except now we could afford the small portable tape recorders instead of the cumbersome models of 1958.

Fifty patients, ranging in age from thirty-seven to seventy-four (mean of 58), comprise our sample. All were admitted to the unit with the diagnosis of proven or suspected myocardial infarction. Thirty-five were males, and fifteen were females. Their average time in the coronary-care unit was four and eight-tenths days. Four died during the study. Patients were selected in a random fashion. The only criterion for inclusion was the ability to speak English. Thirty-seven were general hospital patients in a four-bed intensive care floor. The four-bed ward was a cramped, essentially windowless place, as cheerless and drab as a room in a tenement. Beds were separated by heavy, retractable, ceiling-to-floor curtains. There was no sound proofing. Sexes were mixed. The chief difference between the ward and private accommodations was privacy.

In the four-bed ward monitors were placed on a wall shelf above and behind the patient's bed. This made it difficult for the patient to observe his own oscilloscope but easy to see his neighbor's. In the private rooms the monitor was on a bedside cart with the cathode screen usually visible. Constant intravenous therapy was carried out on all patients, and most had indwelling urethral catheters. Vital signs were taken hourly or more often, invariably awakening each patient.

The Setting   FINDINGS

Not one of the forty-eight patients questioned spontaneously complained about the atmosphere of the unit. Upon being asked specifically, eight agreed that the quarters were small or depressing or both. Six of the eight were lifelong claustrophobes. We could elicit no suggestions for improving the design of the unit, and most patients preferred to have no television or music. Despite the frequency of positive responses, most patients are glad to leave the unit when their time comes. We believe the absence of complaints comes from the fear of complaining.

Cardiac Monitor

Twenty-six of the fifty patients questioned were reassured by the bedside presence of the monitor. Eighteen were neutral to its presence, and six disliked it. There was a trend indicating that women respond more positively than men to the monitor's presence. Thirty-nine did not object to the monitor's sound (3 found it comforting), and eleven considered it annoying.

Fourteen wanted to watch their own electrocardiographic tracings and made an effort to do so even though it meant twisting about uncomfortably to look over their shoulders. Three objected to seeing their oscilloscope patterns, and the remainder were neutral to it. Sixteen patients enjoyed watching the monitor of others; this group included five patients who did not want to observe their own. Nearly without exception they interpreted their neighbor's tracings as being worse than their own. Men were far more interested than women in watching the oscilloscope.

There was no apparent correlation between the patient's knowledge of the monitor's purpose and his response to its sight, sound, or presence.

The alarm accidentally sounded for nineteen patients. The fact that only five of them admitted being frightened may be the result of previous explanations of the monitor's function and anticipation of the possibility of false alarm.

Mood

Judgments of predominant mood for each of the fifty patients were made from comments in the hospital chart, nursing notes, observations by relatives, impressions of the investigator, and subjective reports from the patient himself. At least two corroborating sources were required to confirm each investigator's observation. There was no disagreement between these sources.

Anxiety was judged to be present when the patient complained of being anxious or when he appeared nervous, sweaty, fidgety, restless, or constantly asked for reassurance or sedation. Agitation, as we use the term, refers to patients who were notably hyperactive and whose motor restlessness evoked comment from all who cared for them. Depression was judged to be present either when the patient appeared despondent and was seen to cry or if he admitted to sadness or discouragement during the interview.

Forty of the fifty patients were judged anxious. Eight were agitated, and eleven expressed anger at fate or circumstance; hostility, however, was seldom directed against individuals. Twenty-nine admitted being depressed or exhibited behavior consistent with depression. The depression was a reaction to coronary disease and judged to range from mild to moderate in intensity. In no case was the depressive reaction incapacitating; none of the patients required psychiatric treatment after discharge for the six-month period of our follow-up observation, although at least 25 per cent could have profited from it. Although the fact may be incidental, all four of the patients who died during our study were rated as depressed.

Witnessing Cardiac Arrest

Eleven of the fifty witnessed a fatal cardiac arrest. Seven of these denied fear either during or after the arrest. Only three admitted fear. These data were not collected on the eleventh patient. The initial response to watching the arrest was irritability and annoyance at the patient affected. This was rapidly followed by astonishment at the efficiency of the arrest team. All who witnessed the event described the activity with remarkable clarity. Sounds and imagination must have been involved because most accounts came through as if the bed curtain had not been drawn. For example, one patient "knew the doctor was massaging the heart." Another "knew they were opening the chest."

In neither case was a thoracotomy performed, and the bed curtains were pulled shut in both.

One patient was reassured by the arrest drill because the victim was an elderly woman. He mused that if they did that much for her, they would go all out for him because he was so much younger. When asked if he worried more about himself after seeing the arrest he replied, "Oh, no, she was an old lady." Although empathy for the victim was expressed by all eleven, none identified with the patient affected.

One unobtrusive measure that witnessing cardiac arrest may not be as benign an experience as some patients describe has to do with room preference for readmission. We asked each patient whether he would prefer private or ward accommodations should they return to the hospital. All ward patients, with the exception of those who had witnessed an arrest, picked the four-bed ward as their choice. Those who had viewed the arrest preferred a solitary room.

Survival of Cardiac Arrest

Nine of the fifty had cardiac arrest. Three died without recovering consciousness, and six survived; one, however, for only thirteen days. Only two could remember anything about the event. A male patient vaguely recalled being thumped on the chest and hearing doctors' voices. The second, a woman, was unsure whether what she reported really happened or took place in a dream. "A funny experience . . . a hand down my throat squeezing my heart . . . I felt it was happening . . . but I don't know if it happened in a dream." Two patients had nightmares immediately after the arrest. A woman dreamed of smothering in a fire and a man being caught trying to smoke cigarettes. The fire dreams have also been reported by Druss and Kornfeld (6). Two others had nightmares only after they returned home. One blamed sleeping medication for her bad dreams because they stopped when her bedtime barbiturate was discontinued. The other patient complained of "troubled dreams" that stopped once she returned to work. Traumatic neuroses with chronic anxiety and emotional invalidism have not developed in the three patients who are alive at the six-month follow-up interval. Two have returned to work, whereas the third remains inactive because of physical disability. One of the two who died after leaving the hospital had signs of chronic anxiety and overdependency on his wife; the other man was emotionally stable until his death.

None of the six considered themselves unique as a result of having survived a period of heart stoppage. Two regarded their arrests as the equivalent of dying but did not elaborate on this even when urged to do so by the investigator.

Being Given Last Rites

Thirty patients, twenty-two men and eight women ranging from thirty to seventy-four were interviewed shortly after receiving this sacrament. There was no difference in mortality between this group and a comparison population who had not been given last rites. Twenty-three admitted anxiety directly or were rated as anxious by the investigator. Sixteen expressed thoughts referable to death or dying. At least four said they were sure they were going to die on the way to the emergency ward. Twenty-six of the thirty patients responded positively to last rites. Thirteen did not qualify their favorable response while thirteen admitted to experiencing anxieties or expressed some criticism of the procedure but remained firm in their endorsement of it. Positive responders saw the procedure as something important and reassuring. For those who were ambivalently positive, the experience clearly had frightening aspects. The response of four patients was primarily anxious or negative.

The most threatening aspect of these rites had to do with the way they were presented. When the priest was calm and emphasized the routine nature of the sacrament, that it was administered to every one with heart trouble, little protest occurred. Referring to it as the sacrament of the sick rather than Last Rites was also helpful.

Women patients seemed to respond more positively than men, private patients more so than ward patients. Those whose religion was important in premorbid life were the best responders.

The following is a humorous example of how the Last Rites should not be done but how the patient managed to save the day, nonetheless.

A seventy-two-year-old boiler room worker, admitted with his first myocardial infarction, said, "The priest came in and told me 'I come in a rush,' he says, 'they just called me up and told me . . . they got you in here, so I come in to anoint you.' 'Whaddya mean,' I says, 'anoint me? Anoint me for what?' He says, 'For death!' He says, 'We can't be too careful . . . because anybody with a heart attack can shuffle out in no time.' You know? . . . I laughed. We joked about it for a few minutes. He told me, 'Well, it's just a matter of form, we've got to anoint everybody with a heart condition . . . they're liable to die right away!' So he went through all the formalities and I bid him goodbye." The patient's wife said that he was "frightened when they anointed him," but the patient denied this. Both thought, however, that the priest's presentation could have been improved. Even so, they stressed that being anointed was the most important thing. Said the patient, "Everybody seriously sick should be anointed."

Defense Mechanisms

Twenty of the fifty were major deniers; twenty-six were partial deniers while four we labeled minimal deniers. These latter individuals, the minimal deniers, were not exactly fearful. They may not complain of anxiety but will admit to it on being asked and present no consistent criteria for denial. When they attempt it, they fail to make denial work.

Denial is apt to be more evident when the alternative is to acknowledge fear. For example, twenty-eight of forty-five patients admitted they had thought of death during confinement in the unit; however, only eleven of forty-two admitted experiencing fear during that time. Consequently, it appears that thoughts of dying do not necessarily produce an admission of fear in these patients.

Statistical analysis of our data demonstrated no significant relation between denial and the patient's mood. Anxiety, depression, hostility, and agitation were equally dispersed among the deniers. Neither age nor sex correlated significantly with the patient's use of denial. However, there was a definite trend for deniers to respond positively to the cardiac monitor. None of the minimal deniers found monitoring reassuring.

Although the numbers are small, it is noteworthy that an inverse relation exists between denial and mortality. Not one major denier died during the study; two of the four deaths were in minimal deniers. The minimal denier, representing 8 per cent of the total sample, contributed 50 per cent of the mortality. Chi-square analysis (Fisher's Exact Test) shows this relation to be significant beyond the 5 per cent level.

DISCUSSION

Subsequent work with another class of patients sustaining a recent acute myocardial infarction has been recently completed. These are fifty individuals of comparable age, severity of illness, and sex but of higher socioeconomic status. They were hospitalized in a much more pleasantly situated private CCU. All rooms are occupied by one patient only and they are as airy, light, and as cheery as such a habitation can be. We had been advised by colleagues as well as informed by a previous writing(8) in the field to expect considerable differences in the responses between white- and blue-collar types. Socioeconomic factors are supposed to play a large role in the way patients respond to myocardial infarctions. By and large our experience has not borne this out. Both categories tend to deny to the same extent. However, there are more major deniers in blue-collar workers, perhaps because to them admitting fear is more shameful than to the educated. Oddly enough, there are no minimal deniers among the white collars. The history of previous myocardial infarction had no effect on the extent of denial. Once a major denier, always a major denier.

One of the consistent findings in both socioeconomic groups is that the thought of death, or the realization that one is in danger of dying, by no means produces the fear of death. Two examples stand out to support this.

> A fifty-three-year-old surgeon experienced severe chest pain while waiting for a plane. It passed within a few minutes and he gave it no further thought until he was airborne. At this point the pain returned along with dyspnea. He called the stewardess for oxygen and announced he had a heart attack. By the time the air craft put down an ambulance was waiting. His pain had crescendoed and he fully realized that he was having a myocardial infarction. He also recalls with some puzzlement that the fear of death was not once experienced through the entire stage of his acute illness. It was only later in convalescence that concern about returning to a full work load began to worry him and cause him to wonder how much life he had left.

Another man, in his late twenties, developed severe chest pain while lifting bulk cargo on a part-time job. He had been expecting a heart attack because his schedule had included full-time school plus a physically exhausting moonlighting job. Within ten minutes of his attack he had called his wife to say that he was heading for the hospital with a myocardial infarction and had lined up a friend to drive him. On the way he sensed his end was near and had to fight back the desire to return home for a last look at his two children. With a great effort of will he continued to the hospital. At one point he felt close to passing out and considered asking his friend to give mouth to mouth breathing but declined; the friend was too skittish to be effective. Eventually, he arrived near shock, fully aware that every breath might be his last but again like the previous case, feeling no fear of death whatsoever yet having no explanation for its absence. The only possible reason for this lack was his intense concern with pain. However, when pain relief was obtained, fear did not take its place.

I would like to add a few closing notes. We have a mass of data that is still in the process of being analyzed. Much of it is conflictual and very few rules of thumb can be extracted.

The denial of fear, totally or in part, seems to be one of the main coping mechanisms these patients use in life-threatening circumstances. We view denial as a process that aims at minimizing fear and utilizes any number of defences, such as rationalizing, isolating affect or displacement to attain its end. It is interpersonal as well as intrapersonal and probably varies in extent and effectiveness depending upon who the patient addresses. In the coronary care unit, the majority of personnel do, of course, bolster the patient's denial at every step along the way, so that it is bound to be more effective than in situations where it is challenged.

Until we have suitable neurophysiological, biochemical, and psychological indices to support or refute our clinical impressions we can only say that denial seems to work. Soon, we hope to correlate major denial against short-term and long-term morbidity and mortality. We are also interested in the role denial plays in fending off depression. Depression is a more serious consequence of late convalescence, when the patient returns to work and finds his functioning impaired; it seldom is a grave problem in the coronary care unit.

As a final thought, I would like to add that neither Dr. Cassem nor I are pleased with the word "denial." It sounds like a negative quality, a negation, when, in fact, what it may mirror is the presence of something far more positive. We have heard people allude to the life force and we have been asked if denial might represent it. Does the denial of fear mean an affirmation of life? It certainly could. Perhaps it is a flight into health. However, compelling and attractive a term like life force is, we have nothing to measure it by as yet and, as a consequence, are forced to retain the concept of denial because it is workable, definable, and measurable.

REFERENCES

1. BROWNE, I.W., and HACKETT, T.P.: Emotional reactions to threat of impending death: study of patients on monitor cardiac pacemaker. *Irish J Med Sc, 6* (496):177-187, 1967.
2. WEISMAN, A.D., and HACKETT, T.P.: Predilection to death: death and dying as psychiatric problem. *Psychosom Med, 23*:232-256, 1961.
3. HACKETT, T.P.; CASSEM, N.H., and WISHNIE, H.A.: The coronary-care unit: An appraisal of its psychologic hazards. *New Eng J Med, 279*:1365-1370, (December 19) 1968.
4. McKEGNEY, F.P.: Intensive care syndrome: definition, treatment and prevention of new "disease of medical progress." *Conn Med, 30*:633-636, 1966.
5. NAHUM, L.H.: Madness in recovery room from open-heart surgery or "They kept waking me up." *Conn Med, 29*:771, 1965.
6. DRUSS, R.G., and KORNFELD, D.S.: Survivors of cardiac arrest: psychiatric study. *JAMA, 201*:291-296, 1967.
7. CASSEM, N.H.; WISHNIE, H.A., and HACKETT, T.P.: How coronary patients respond to Last Rites. *Postgrad Med, 45*:147-152, 1969.
8. ROSEN, J.L., and BIBRING, G.L.; Psychological reactions of hospitalized male patients to a heart attack: Age and social-class differences. *Phychosom Med 28*:808-821, 1966.

Chapter 3

PSYCHOLOGICAL RESPONSE
TO CONCENTRATION CAMP SURVIVAL

PAUL CHODOFF

Homo homini lupus . . . man is a wolf to man. The bloody chronicles of recorded history have, time after time, demonstrated the truth of this bitter adage, but never more clearly than in the treatment of the Jewish minority under their control by the German Nazis of the Hitlerian Reich. Therefore, in a symposium on the psychological aspects of stress, the concentration camp experience can serve as a paradigm of how the human organism reacts to stressful conditions which approach the outermost limits of human adaptability and the sustained consequences of such stress.

All of the concentration camps set up by the S.S. in Germany and occupied Europe were not alike and the differences between extermination camps and labor camps were certainly significant. However, the conditions faced by the inmates of all concentration camps can only be described, in the words of A. P. J. Taylor, as "loathsome beyond belief." In addition to the out and out extermination measures, the physical stresses endured by the prisoners included malnutrition, crowding, sleeplessness, exposure, inadequate clothing, forced labor, beatings, injury, torture, exhaustion, medical experimentation, diarrhea, various epidemic diseases, and the effects of the long "death marches" from the camps in the closing days of the War. The physically depleted state of the prisoners, the brutal and primitive conditions in which they lived, and the entirely inadequate medical facilities

Note: This chapter is reproduced by permission of the *Archives of General Psychiatry*. From Chodoff, Paul: The German concentration camp as a psychological stress. *Arch Gen Psychiat*, 1970 (in press).

were responsible for an extremely high death rate and also had the effect of increasing the susceptibility of the inmates to the nonphysical stresses which they had to face. Chief among these latter was the danger to life, ever present and unavoidable. It is possible, to some degree, for a healthy personality to defend itself against a peril which, though very grave, is predictable and is at least potentially limited in time, as in the case of soldiers in combat who can at least hope for relief and rotation out of the fighting zone, but for the concentration camp inmate, as has been described by Viktor Frankl from his own experiences in Auschwitz(1), the absolute uncertainty of his condition was a barrier to the erection of adequate psychological adaptive measures. In addition to the threat to life, the prisoners had to face the catastrophic trauma of separation from their families, thus to the agonizing uncertainty about their own futures was added equally agonizing doubts about whether they would ever see their relatives again. The very least price one had to pay to survive in the camps was to suffer the grossest kind of daily humiliation at the hands of an organization superbly qualified to mete out humiliation. Massive frustration of their basic drives had the apparent dual effect of driving the sexual life of the prisoners underground and of rendering the insistent demands of hunger all-dominating so that fantasies about food occupied much of their conscious awareness. If not himself the victim of casual violence or deliberate cruelty, the prisoner at least frequently witnessed such exhibitions. Since it was impossible to retaliate effectively he had to smother his aggressive feelings, for even the appearance of resentment against the torturers could lead to his own destruction. Regimented, imprisoned, without a moment of privacy during the twenty-four hours, the prisoner's human worth, and even his sense of an individual human identity, was under constant and savage assault. His entire environment was designed to impress upon him his utter, his protoplasmic worthlessness, a worthlessness which had no relationship to what he did, only to what he was. Reduced from individual human status to the status of a debased being, identified not by name but by a number and a badge of a particular color, a conviction of his ineluctable inferiority was hammered into the prisoner by the S.S. jailers who needed to justify their own behavior by convincing themselves of the inferior, sub-human status of the Jews in their charge. The concentration camp inmates lived in a Kafkaesque world in which the rules governing their existence were senseless, capricious, and often mutually con-tradictory, as, for instance, when impossible standards of cleanli-ness were demanded, while, at the same time, the inadequate oppor-tunities and senseless rules about toileting made even an elementary decency impossible.

At this point, I am going to interpose a description, recorded in her own words at my request, of some aspects of life at Auschwitz by a former inmate who has also been a patient of mine. I believe that this account will convey to you, in a far more meaningful way than the essentially abstract summary I have given you, something of the physical and psychological stresses which confronted the concentration camp inmate, as well as a suggestion of the adaptive measures called forth by these stresses.

> We arrived to Auschwitz in the early part of April. That's a story by itself—the arrival and the happenings—you know, the selections were quite an experience by itself. We lived in blocks. It's called a block in German but it's a barracks and it has 1,500 people and the bar-racks had rows and rows of three tiers-bunk beds—they were very poorly built, out of just boards and lumber and each bunk bed had twelve people—in our case twelve women, and we happened to choose the upper bunk because we thought it would be the best. It was OK for us but it caused an awful lot of heartache afterwards because, as I said, the bunk beds were not built very well and the boards broke un-der the weight of us in the beginning before we started losing weight and there were many broken or fractured skulls or bones below us. Each person had a blanket. We were supposed to have a blanket. It so happened that the blankets were stolen so we never ended up with enough blankets for all of us. Maybe by the end of the evening we would have two or three blankets left for twelve people. I think the biggest crisis after the days hardship was finding a blanket to sleep on and the fights we had keeping the blanket. I must say I was one of the lucky (I say lucky) or exceptional persons who was an assis-tant to the Capo. It came very handy at the time. I suffered an awful lot because of it later, but it gave me protection, maybe I had the blanket . . . I don't even remember because all this did not matter. Anyway, we got up at two o'clock in the morning and I don't know who awakened us—the girls who brought the coffee in big barrels. It

was black and it had charcoal in it and maybe chicory. I have no idea only maybe chicory was too good for us . . . it was rather lukewarm and they thought it was enough to hold us through the day. And no one wanted the coffee. I think its like the Army. You would rather have an hour sleep or so, but you had to have it. The barracks had to be emptied, and we had to get back and line up for the appel and that was my job, getting people up. I was assigned to three or four bunks and that means I was assigned to wake up approximately a hundred fifty to two hundred people who did not want to face the day's reality. I mean, because we knew what was coming. So I was up, pulling blankets off of people—"get up," screaming, carrying on, even hitting. Once I hit someone and she looked at me and it was one of my mother's friends. I apologized. I felt terribly bad. I kept on doing it. I got them up. I think the whole process took nearly half an hour to make 1,500 people get out of the block. We were up but there was no question of clothing because we got one dress when we entered Auschwitz and I got a very, very long petticoat. It came all the way down to my ankle. It came very handy because I was able to use it little by little as a toilet tissue because it was nonexistent, 'till there was nothing left. So I just had a dress to wear and I think most people, that's all they had, and shoes and a toothbrush that hung around my neck. It was my most prized thing . . . a toothbrush. I don't know how I got it but I got it and yes, I did get up. I know I got out my bunk, got up a half an hour earlier than any one else because we were determined to keep clean and we got up and we went to the washroom that was at least, oh, two or three bunkers away from us and we stripped ourself completely naked and scrubbed ourselves with cold water because we didn't want any lice on us. We checked our clothes for lice, because typhus was spreading already at that time and, anyway, we had to line up for appel—roll call, and the 1,500 people were divided in three groups so that means I had five hundred people to line up and in each line I think there were maybe ten, fifteen, I'm not sure. But somehow, I don't know how the rumor started, but someone gave the word that they were going to pick so many people to be cremated—that the first four or five rows are going to be taken to be cremated. Well, I tried to get anyone to get in the first five rows. It was impossible. I had to make them do it. My friends and my mother did stay. They stayed put where they were supposed to. Not that we didn't believe in the rumor, but we just happened to be all the time on the first, front line. I was shoving and pushing. But we were lined up around two-thirty in the morning and the Germans did not come out till six o'clock—five or six o'clock I think it was for the appel and there were thirty thousand people in the c lager and it took them a while. They must have made mistake as far as counting the people . . . but I know they always miscounted because, after the first counting was over we were being punished for someone was missing. We had to get down on our knees with our hands up and wait till they counted over and over and over and over till they decided that they got a number. But meantime, we didn't have the big selections when Mengele came around, just the little officers did their jobs and decided a girl with a pimple on her face or someone who was a little bit more run down than should be or with a little bandage. Naturally those people were taken out automatically to the crematorium. So we had to be very careful that you shouldn't have any scars showing or you should look fresh and not unwell. Well, this appel could have lasted sometimes till eleven or twelve noon . . . so by eleven or twelve we were allowed to come in to our bunks and then lunch time came. We got a slice of bread and a piece of margarine and that's all. It is very hard for me to recall food—what we ate or not because I decided that all those things are unimportant. That I am going to have control over my body, that food is not important, so I can't remember, but I think it was one slice of bread and a slice of margarine in it and some kind of jelly made out of red beets. Then we were supposed to take a walk or do something. I think in all my eight months that I have been there, maybe twice we were able to take a walk because we were being punished for one reason or the other and we had to stay in our bunks, or a new transport came in and they would not allow us out to watch the transport coming in and we were locked in our block or barracks and so the days were spent in the barracks. Then it came the evening roll call. That started about two o'clock in the afternoon and then again the same circus-lining up, waiting, miscounting and counting, and counting, and counting and it was seven to eight o'clock in the evening before evening meal came and before we were allowed to come in, sometimes nine-thirty or ten o'clock. I mean it all depended how good of a counter they were and naturally we never passed unpunished. If someone was missing we were punished by kneeling. Otherwise we stood—and we had to stand sometimes in hot sun and sometimes in rain. I don't even remember, I must have had shoes—I guess I had shoes, but anyway, evening came around and then we had our meal. The meal consisted of mush. It was some kind of a liquid, thickened with something. I doubt if it was flour. It had a few potatoes in the bottom of the barrel and then it had some kind of a chemical taste to it that the women decided it was some kind of a tranquilizer, but I doubted the Germans spent money on putting tranquilizers in. But another thing, we stopped menstruating and they thought that, whatever chemical taste it had in it, this is the thing that stopped us from menstruating so we didn't menstruate at all. I didn't menstruate until I was liberated and I don't know what it was, but anyway, each cup had eight ounces of that mush. Again, I was one of the lucky ones who distributed the food. I think I was fair.

I tried . . . I was fair when it came to distributing food—I did not, I would not allow myself to bring any more up to my bunk than we were allowed except my mother who was quite ill—she had diarrhea and she could not digest the food. She enjoyed the potatoes and she was weakening. She was getting weaker and weaker day by day. You know she was at that time forty-three years old and it is hard to think of it that here I reach the age and how would I have been able, how would I have reacted under the circumstances that she did at this age. I feel very young, by the way. But she seemed to me very old at that time and well anyway, evening meal over, we were allowed to take a walk. But again, when transports were coming in they locked the doors and there was complete curfew and we were not allowed to go out and we were just, well, listening to the screams or the silence or the smell of the burning flesh and wondering what tomorrow was going to bring to us. Some were wondering. I knew I am going to make it. The human torture, getting up in the morning and things, smelling the burning flesh and the flying soot. The air was oily, greasy. There were no birds.

I just want to describe one thing. I would like to talk about this. I had a very good friend, a childhood friend. He is now a professor at a university. He teaches physics and he attended the seminary with Einstein. He was the first boy who discovered me, that I was a girl at thirteen and I didn't like him and he was in the concentration camp too and his sister was in my camp. His little sister who was a year or two younger than I was and why I bring him up because he comes to Washington once a year to attend a physics convention and we meet and he is plagued. I mean he doesn't talk about his experiences in Auschwitz. He wants to know about his sister, his little sister. What happened to his little sister, and I always say she was a lady. Till the last moment she was just a lady just like at home. They came from a very wealthy aristocratic Jewish family and they were all surgeons, the father and grandfather, grandparents each. They all followed the same line. Anyway, he always asks, "My little sister, how was she?" He wants to know more and more about her and the only answer is she was a lady. There were the rare moments where we were allowed to walk and you know, in Europe we used to promenade in the evenings and his little sister with her girlfriend just promenaded just like at home. Just like nothing happened, with the same poise, the little girl who has been brought up by the governess and her posture has not changed. The rags didn't mean a thing, she was still a queen.

Meantime, sometimes I went to the fence with my boyfriend. My boyfriend happened to be working in the crematorium. He was a lawyer. He was assigned to work there and he was in the next camp and just the road and the wire separated us and so we were able to talk to each other. His letters were very important. He sent all his

experience. The letters he wrote about his experinces and his feelings
being in the Sommer Commando. He was among the group of people
who cremated—they were in charge of cremation, of killing, of putting the dionide in the shower rooms and then taking the bodies, pulling the teeth, the gold teeth and anything valuable out of the dead
bodies and cremating them and he used to write to me letters every
day. And then in the evening we talked and he told me who went,
and what was going to happen tomorrow. He knew. And you see
those Sommer Commandos, they were allowed to live for three
months and after three months they were killed too, because the Germans would not allow to leave a trace behind them. So while it was
good to see him, he would never allow me to forget where I was and
what to expect, and he made me very, very much aware of the danger of the situation that we were in, and he tried to persuade me to
leave Auschwitz and leave my mother behind me and get out from
there because I wouldn't have any future. I would be cremated if I
would stay there and I was afraid and he put ambivalent feelings in
my mind as far as my mother was concerned. All of a sudden my
mother became a burden. I felt she weighed me down. She kept me
back, but I did not leave her. Well, one day I received a letter from
him and it was a good-bye letter. He told me that they are going to
explode the crematorium because his three months were up and they
had nothing to lose. They would try to escape if they can, but, as I
said, they had nothing to lose. So I was up at night and the trouble is
that no one believed me. My friends from the bunk, they thought I
was crazy, because I was filled with anxiety, screaming, carrying on.
And then we did hear the explosion and next day we saw the smoke
of the burning crematoriums—you could see the crematorium from
our lager. You could see where it was just a little bit damaged and
we heard that they tried to escape and they almost made it and they
were caught and that was the end of them.

I think they were very worried about our physical well-being and
cleanliness so we had to be shaved. That's right, several times while I
stayed in Auschwitz, we were shaved of hair—head, under arms and
intimate parts of our body by Jewish inmates—standing, we were
standing on a stool that the Jewish inmates should be able to reach us
easier and surrounded by S.S. men who seemed to enjoy it very much.
Well it didn't bother me either. I had no feelings whatsoever. I
couldn't care less at this point of the game. It really didn't matter.

As I said, we had selections every single day—some just slight—just
picking people out as I mentioned before because of scars, because of
pimples, because of being run down, because of looking tired or because of having a crooked smile or because someone just didn't like
you. But then they were beginning to liquidate Auschwitz and we had
major selections where you were selected either to go to work or to

the crematorium and in this case Dr. Mengele was involved in it. He was quite an imposing figure and his presence—I don't think everybody was scared because, rather I wasn't. I was hypnotized by his looks, by his actions. The barracks had two massive doors and we were inside. They did not let us out. It was in October and it was rainy and we were holding pots of water—we didn't sleep because of the rain because we had to keep ourselves dry, and then the doors swing open quite dramatically, great entrance with Mengele in the center accompanied by two S.S. women and a couple of soldiers and he stands with his whip on one side and his legs apart. It's unbelievable. It looked like Otto Preminger arranged the theme for the whole thing. It seems to me now that it was like a movie. Anyway the Capo came out and she gave us orders to undress and line up in front of the barracks. It had two rooms. One was a storage room and one was the Capo's room—and Mengele stood in between and he had one leg lifted on a stool, his right leg, and he was leaning on his knee and he had a switch in the same hand and while we were lining up I was able to observe what he was doing. Till I had to face him I really had no feelings. I couldn't describe how I felt but I saw the switch go. The whip, rather. It was a horse whip—left, right and I noticed that those who were motioned left were in a better condition, physical condition than the ones who were motioned to go right. Anyway, this went on and on and not a sound, even if it meant life or death. I don't know how other people felt about it, but I was quite well informed, I was accused of being able to face the truth, of being able to know because I had my mother with me. The others said it was easy for me to believe all this because I had my mother with me. I had no great loss. They loved their mothers, they care, and they wanted to believe their mothers are safe somewhere in another bunk, somewhere in another camp. It made them stronger, knowing their parents were not cremated, but I had my mother and I knew my father was OK at that time in another bunk at camp. Anyway, my turn came. I had a choice to make. Not only Mengele had a choice to make, I had. I had to make up my mind. Am I going to follow my mother or is this it? Am I going to separate from her? The only way I was able to work out the problem was I am not going to give a chance for myself to decide. He will have to decide. I will go ahead in front of my mother—that was unusual, she being my mother, out of courtesy I followed her all the time in any other circumstances, but in this case I was going first and my mother followed me and I went. I think my heart was beating quite fast, not because I was afraid—I knew I would come through, but because I was doing something wrong. I was doing something terribly wrong. Anyway I passed Mengele. I didn't see him. I just passed and I was sent into the room where I would be kept alive and I turned around and my mother was with me, so this was a very happy ending.

As I said in the evenings if I had a chance I went over to talk to my friend—to the fence, to the electric fence, and at each end of the fence they had the watch towers where the Nazis were able to observe us and—just for the fun of it—the girl who was right next to me—I think they just wanted to see if they can aim well because I don't know why but they shot her right in the eye, and she lost her eye. Another time another girl was at the same place. Her friend threw a package of food over to her and she ran towards the fence to catch it and she touched the wire and there she hung. She looked like Jesus Christ spread out with her two arms stuck to the wire—and, that's all.

In the end, people were losing weight, and they were getting skinnier and skinnier and some of them were just skeletons but I really did not see them. I just wiped the pictures out of my mind. I was able to step over them and when I came out from the concentration camp I said I did not see a dead body—I mean, I feel that I didn't see them. Even if I can see them. This is what's killing me now that I have never felt the strain, the brutality, the physical brutality of the concentration camp. I mean like my aunt, my young aunt, was thirteen or fourteen, who has been exposed at this early age of her life to brutality and death and she talks with a passion of what they did to her and then when I meet another woman who is in her sixties and she will tell me her sufferings, I can't stand them. I broke all the friendship up with them. I don't want them. I can't stand them, because they bore me. I . . . they bore me. I just can't stand listening to them, and I have nothing to do with them.

What enabled a man or woman to survive such a hell? We have no real answers to this question and must resort to such generalizations as the almost miraculous and infinite adaptability of the human species. It needs to be emphasized that while particular varieties of individual defensive and coping behavior played a role in whether a prisoner would live or die, such behavior was far less important than were such chance factors as where the prisoner happened to be when a "selection" for the gas chamber was taking place or the mood of the selector at the time.

However, accounts by survivors do agree in describing a fairly consistent sequence of reactions to concentration camp life. This sequence was inaugurated by a universal response of shock and terror on arrival at the camp, since the S.S. made it their business to impress the new prisoner with their malevolent power, while many of the old prisoners, displaying "the camp mentality," manifested by irritability, egotistical behavior, and envy, were often cold and unsympathetic to new arrivals. This fright reaction was generally followed by a period of apathy, and, in most cases, by a longer period of mourning and depression. The period of apathy was often psychologically protective, in that it served to provide a kind of transitional emotional hibernation, but, in some cases, apathy took over to such an extent that the prisoner became a "mussulman," who gave up the struggle to live and did not survive very long.

Among those prisoners who continued to struggle for life, certain adaptive measures gradually gained ascendancy and came to be characteristic of the long-term adjustment. Regressive behavior, of greater or lesser degree, was almost universal, being induced in the prisoners by the overwhelming infantilizing pressures to which they were subjected and by the need to stifle aggressive impulses. As a consequence of the complete reversal of values in the camps, it is likely that such behavior served an adaptive function, since regressive prisoners immersed in fantasies were likely to be docile and submissive toward the S.S. and thus to have a better chance of escaping retaliatory measures. A consequence of such regression was that many prisoners, like children, became quite dependent on their savage masters, so that attitudes toward the S.S. were marked more by ambivalence than by conscious overt hostility. Some prisoners went so far as to employ the well-known mechanism of identification with the aggressor, imitating the behavior and taking on the values of the S.S. In the dreams of more than one female survivor whom I have examined, S.S. troopers were always tall, handsome, and god-like figures, and I believe you will be able to detect elements of such a reaction in the description of my patient's encounter with Dr. Mengele. Those who have seen or read the play, *The Deputy*, will remember the satanic figure of "The Doctor" who was modeled on the same Doctor Mengele, "The Angel of Death of Auschwitz," whom I have heard described in such awed terms by survivors of Auschwitz that I, who have never seen him, can visualize his tall, radiant, immaculately dressed figure sitting nonchalantly astride a chair as, like Osiris, the judge of the Kingdom of the Dead, he gestures with his riding whip selecting the prisoners lined up in front of him for either death or life.

It appears that the most important personality defenses among concentration camp inmates were denial and isolation of affect. As might be expected in the case of this probably most ubiquitous of all defenses, there was widespread employment of denial as manifested by my patient who would not see the corpses she was stepping over and by the poignant picture of her fellow inmates who refused to believe that the smoke arising from the crematorium chimneys came from the burning corpses of their mothers. Isolation of affect, which could be so extreme as to involve a kind of emotional anesthesia, seemed to have functioned particularly to protect the ego against the dangers associated with feelings of hostility toward an external object which treats the self as if it were an inanimate thing and not a person. My patient who says, "It doesn't bother me. I had no feelings whatsoever," when being shaved while naked in front of S.S. troopers was certainly isolating her affect from her cognition. When combined with an ability to observe themselves and their surroundings, this kind of tamping down of affect along with sublimatory processes helped such gifted individuals as Frankl(1), Elie Cohen (2), and Bettelheim(3), to produce some rather remarkably objective reports of life in the camps. Some form of companionship with others was indispensable, since a completely isolated individual could not have survived in the camps, but the depth of such companionship was usually limited by the overpowering egotistical demands of self-preservation, except in certain political and religious groups. Daydreams of revenge served the purpose of swallowing up some of the submerged aggression, while aggression could also be discharged through quarrelsome and irritable behavior toward the other prisoners, as illustrated by the description of the fighting over food and blankets and by projection on the S.S. who were then seen as even more formidable, endowed as they thus were with the unexpressed hostility of the prisoners. Since the existence of mental illness of any degree of severity would have been incompatible with survival, an interesting adaptive consequence of imprisonment was that new psychosomatic or psychoneurotic disorders rarely developed while already existing ones often markedly improved, and suicide, except under conditions as to be almost indistinguishable from murder, was also an infrequent phenomenon.

As soon after the end of the War and liberation as the recovery of some physical health permitted, most survivors made their way back to their homes. More often than not, their worst fears were confirmed, and they usually found that not only had their relatives and friends perished in the holocaust, but they also found their homes and communities destroyed or uninhabitable. Such frustrating and disappointing aspects of postliberation reality were responsible for the inevitable disruption of the rosy fantasies of postwar life which had proliferated during the imprisonment and which have been called "the postdisaster Utopia" (4). In the regressed state of most of the ex-prisoners at this stage, such a narcissistic blow, as well as real disappointment of their idealistic hopes that a better world would now arise from the ruins of Europe, resulted in much bitterness, resentment, and depression, even, in some cases, in temporary flurries of antisocial or paranoid behavior. A large number of the liberated prisoners, homeless, alone, bewildered, and without resources, took refuge in the D.P. camps which were set up in various parts of Europe, and, in some cases, they remained in them for years with the result that their neurotic symptoms became fixated because of the monotony of D.P. camp life and its fostering of passivity and hypochondriacal preoccupation.

As the immediate postwar epoch drew to a close, the surviving remnant of concentration camp prisoners gradually settled themselves in more or less permanent abodes in their own countries of origin, or in other lands, especially in the United States and Israel. For this latter group, to the multiple traumata they had already endured were now added the need to adjust to a new environment, to new customs, and to a different language.

At this point one might expect the grisly story to come to an end for most of the survivors, with the passage of time allowing the gradual envelopment of their fears and memories in psychic scar tissue. This is not what happened, however, for, as I have described in another publication (5), in the late 1950's and early 1960's articles began to appear in the medical literature of many countries describing features of personality disorder and psychiatric illness

still present many years later in a large number of these survivors
of the holocaust, in some cases cropping up after latent periods of
months or years after the persecution.

Although figures are not available for the overall incidence of
psychiatric sequelae among the survivors of the Nazi persecution,
it is clear, judging from reports from many countries, including
Germany, the United States, Israel, Poland and Norway(5), that
they are of high frequency.

Long-term, unfavorable personality alterations in survivors have
taken two widely overlapping directions. Some individuals develop
tendencies toward seclusiveness, social isolation, helplessness, and
apathy. They are passive, fatalistic, and dependent, wanting only
to be taken care of and to be let alone by a world whose requirements they are no longer interested in trying to fulfill. Other survivors regard their environment with suspicion, hostility, and mis-
trust reflected in their attitudes toward other people which range
from quite, envious bitterness to cynicism and quarrelsome bellig-
erence.

The most distinctive long-term consequence of the Nazi persecution, however, is the concentration camp syndrome. Invariably
present in this syndrome is some degree of felt anxiety along with
irritability, restlessness, apprehensiveness, and a startle reaction to
such ordinary stimuli as an unexpected phone call or a knock at the
door. These anxiety symptoms are almost always worse at night,
and are usually accompanied by insomnia and by nightmares, which
are either simple or only slightly disguised repetitions of the traumatic experiences. Psychosomatic involvement of almost all the
organ systems has been reported, the most common being weakness, fatigue, and gastrointestinal troubles. A very characteristic
feature is an obsessive ruminative state in which the individual is
preoccupied with recollections of his own persecutory experiences
and with the often idealized life with his family before the persecution began. Interviews with concentration camp survivors often
leave the interviewer with the uncanny sensation that he has been
transported in time back to, say, the grey inferno of Auschwitz, so
vivid and compelling is the wealth of detail with which they describe the events which befell them and which they witnessed, so
that the interviewer gets the impression that nothing of real signifi-

cance in their lives has happened since the liberation. This feeling that life was permanently interrupted by the concentration camp period may be why my patient still feels "young" at her present age. Most individuals find their memories unwelcome and obtrusive, but there are a few who actually appear to derive pleasure from them. Depression, at times associated with "survival guilt," is also a very common manifestation of the concentration camp syndrome.

Studies dealing with the very few surviving individuals who were infants or very young children in the concentration camps are particularly interesting. Anna Freud and Sophie Dann have made a fascinating study of a group of six children who had all been in the concentration camp at Theresienstadt before the age of three years(6). When seen in England after the liberation, these children showed severe emotional disturbances and were hypersensitive, restless, aggressive, and difficult to handle, but they had also evolved a remarkably stable sibling group and a group identity during their internment which seemed to protect them against the worst pathogenic effects of the absence of a maternal figure. A follow-up of the later fates of these children indicates that, though they all had stormy experiences during adolescence, most of them achieved some degree of stability by early adulthood. Edith Sterba has reported on a group of twenty-five displaced children and adolescents(7), who had lost both parents and had been in concentration camps or in hiding for three to five years. She describes how attempts to place these children with foster parents were greatly hampered by the disappointment and dissatisfaction expressed by the children toward whatever was done for them. They, too, displayed a desperate need to cling together, apparently deriving more security from these peer relationships than from even the most benevolent relationship with the adults on whom they were displacing all the angry fear engendered in them by the loss of their parents. Among my own cases, there were six who were five years of age or younger in 1939 and who therefore underwent the experiences of the persecution at an extremely early period of their lives. In addition to various degrees of overt psychoneurotic symptomatology, I found them all to be emotionally volatile people whose moods fluctuate markedly and who react to a mild degree of stress, such as an unexpected event, with exacerbations of anx-

iety. Their personalities are marked by various admixtures of a
bitter, cynical, pessimistic attitude toward life and a childlike and
total kind of emotional dependency. Although intimacy and close-
ness are of the greatest importance to them, they tend to show self-
defeating patterns of excessive expectation and bitter or despairing
withdrawal when these expectations are disappointed. They are
extremely sensitive to actual or threatened separation from those
on whom they have become dependent. It seems clear that the most
damaging consequences to the personality maturation of these
individuals resulted from the absence of a reliable and secure interpersonal environment, particularly the lack of adequate mothering
in the early years. This applies not only to those children who lost
both of their natural parents but also to those whose mothers were
forced to appear and disappear actually by force of necessity but
certainly, to the perception of the children, in a cruel and capricious
manner.

To return to the concentration camp syndrome, its nature has
been the subject of some controversy but, on the whole, it appears
reasonable to regard at least the anxiety core of the concentration
camp syndrome as a special variety of traumatic neurosis resembling
in some respects the ordinary combat stress reaction, which is the
paradigm of the traumatic neurosis. A more interesting analogy is
the Japanese A-bomb disease or neurosis described by Lifton in
survivors of the Hiroshima bombing(8), who for many years afterwards have suffered from vague and chronic complaints of fatigue,
nervousness, weakness, and various physical ailments, along with
characterological changes and feelings of what Lifton calls "existential" guilt. Also, although the analogy is not as direct, it is possible, without stretching the bounds of imagination beyond credi-
bility, to draw significant parallels between the concentration camp
experience and the poverty ghettos of our great cities(9).

Although there can be no doubt that the primary cause of the
concentration camp syndrome is the multiple, massive emotional
and physical stress to which the prisoners were exposed during
interment, these stresses cannot alone account for the origins and
development of the later added features of the syndrome or of the
persistence of these symptoms in many cases in spite of the passage
of time and infinitely more favorable circumstances. For such

secondary developments, which differ in character and intensity in different patients, other, additional explanations must be invoked. One theory seeks to ascribe not only the immediate postwar but also the chronic persistent symptoms of the concentration camp syndrome to organic brain disease resulting from injury, illness, and malnutrition incurred during the internment. However, my own experience is in agreement with that of a majority of observers who have reported that brain injury was relatively unimportant in their cases, and that the development and persistence of certain features of the concentration camp syndrome are far more dependent on the immediate and later postwar experiences of the survivor than on organic factors. It is during this postwar period, too, that basic personality strengths and weaknesses would have their effects on the ability of the survivor to cope with what fate might bring his way. Postwar experiences having a significant influence on the ultimate adjustment of the individual include loss of immediate members of family, relatives, homes, and livelihoods, a dashing of the inflated hopes for a postwar Utopia, a long and debilitating residence in D.P. camps, downward change in socioeconomic status, and emigration to strange lands with different language, tempo of life, and customs.

I will conclude this discussion with a consideration of depression and guilt among concentration camp survivors, because these symptoms seem to me to strike to the core of the psychopathology they display and to constitute a kind of existential signature of the persecution. Depression is one of the most characteristic symptoms of concentration camp survivors and, along with the traumatogenic anxiety state and the obsessive rumination over the past, is a hallmark of the concentration camp syndrome. More likely to occur is an unvarying feeling of emptiness, despair, and hopelessness in older people, most of the survivors become depressed episodically, particularly at holidays, anniversaries, and in connection with events which remind them of the past, like the Eichmann trial. It has been suggested that depression may represent a delayed mourning reaction, particularly insistent in its demands because the concentration camp prisoners had been unable to engage in ceremonial mourning for their dead(10). Certainly the brutal destruction of so many family members, relatives, and friends needs no explanation as a cause for

depression, but it is not so obvious why the depression of the concentration camp survivors is so often tinged with feelings of guilt.
In some cases, such feelings are attributed to specific episodes, such
as when a prisoner had taken an action which led to the saving of
his own life at increased risk to another and in such instances it may
be possible to detect the predisposing influence of insufficiently
resolved earlier conflictual experiences. This was true in the case
of the patient whose account of life at Auschwitz you have heard
and certainly in general it would be difficult to devise a more dia-
bolical environment than the concentration camp for fostering
guilt producing conflict over aggressive drives or between self-
preservative and superego impulses. However, there remain a
significant number of ex-concentration camp inmates whose guilt
and depression are attached to nothing more specific than the very
fact that they survived when so many were lost. My encounter
with a large number of survivors of the persecution has left me not
completely satisfied that the depression and guilt they feel can be
explained entirely by the usual combination of precipitating stress
and morbid predisposition which psychiatrists invoke to explain
such symptoms. Perhaps this is because the immense scale of the
tragedy in which these survivors were immeshed seems to render
the ordinary language of psychopathology inadequate and invites
a grander, more transcendent dimension of explication. The stub-
born, even prideful refusal to forget displayed by certain survivors seems to involve something more than masochistic personality mechanisms or a revival of past, incompletely resolved emotional conflicts and, instead, suggests a desperate attempt to rescue
their dead from the limbo of insignificance to which they have been
consigned by bestowing upon their destruction a benison of meaning.

Viktor Frankl himself emerged from Auschwitz with the conviction that the need to find some meaning in an otherwise incom-
prehensible universe constituted an elemental human hunger equal
in importance to other such putative primary motivational forces
as the pleasure principle of Freud(1). In a similar vein, Lifton
found(8) in his study of A-bomb survivors in Hiroshima that for
them the order of the universe had somehow been violated and
that they continued to identify themselves with the dead and be

unable to resolve their guilt through the usual mourning experiences because they could find no spiritual or ideological explanation, no "reason" to explain the disaster and thus to release them from this identification with the dead.

There is an ancient Talmudic legend of the Lamed-Vov, the thirty-six just men who take upon themselves the sufferings of the world. Perhaps those concentration camp survivors who ceaselessly lament the past are performing a similar function and their sufferings can be thought of both as a memorial to their dead and as an act of existential expiation for a species capable of such an outrage upon a common humanness.

REFERENCES

1. FRANKL, V.E.: *Man's Search for Meaning*. Boston, Beacon Press, 1959.
2. COHEN, E.A.: *Human Behavior in the Concentration Camp*. New York, W.W. Norton, 1953.
3. BETTELHEIM, BRUNO: *The Informed Heart*. Glencoe, Free Press, 1960.
4. WOLFENSTEIN, MARTHA: *Disaster*. Glencoe, Free Press, 1957.
5. CHODOFF, P.: Effects of extreme coercive and oppressive forces. In Arieti, Silvano (Ed.): *American Handbook of Psychiatry*. New York, Basic Books, 1966, vol. 3.
6. FREUD, ANNA, and SOPHIE DANN: An experiment in group upbringing. *Psychoanalytic Study of the Child*, 6:122, 1951.
7. STERBA, EDITH: Some Problems of Children and Adolescents Surviving from Concentration Camps. Presented at the Second Wayne State University Conference on the Late Sequelae of Massive Psychic Traumatization, Detroit, Mich., February 21, 1964.
8. LIFTON, ROBERT: Psychological effects of the atomic bomb in Hiroshima. *Daedalus*, Summer 1963.
9. CHODOFF, P.: The Nazi concentration camp and the American poverty ghetto: A comparison. *Proceedings Psychiatric Outpatients Centers of America*, 1967.
10. MEERLOO, JOOST: Delayed mourning in victims of extermination camps. *Journal of the Hillside Hospital, 12*:96, 1963.

Chapter 4

THE PSYCHOLOGICAL ASPECTS
OF EMERGENCY SITUATIONS

ALBERT J. GLASS

THE topic, "Psychological Aspects of Emergency Situations," is concerned with the behavior of relatively uninjured survivors of an emergency situation, be it large or small, and also includes the behavior of individuals involved in rescue, particularly medical personnel. In recent years, there has been a demand for general hospitals to develop plans to handle the overload of injuries from a disaster. Many surveys have indicated that any general hospital can be disorganized and unable to function in emergencies involving the admission of multiple burn and injury cases.

As one would surmise, behavior under emergency conditions is dependent upon a number of variables, such as the nature and intensity of the cause of the emergency, secondary environmental dangers, the presence of others (such as family members), and whether the individuals involved constitute a heterogenous or homogenous group.

TIME MODEL

I would like to approach this problem by using a model which considers behavior over time, so that various phases of behavior can be viewed separately. Such models usually take impact, the actual emergency situation, as the point of reference and utilizes phases before and after impact. The *pre-impact phase* is present when impact becomes probable, e.g. an individual is assigned to Viet Nam or perhaps is drafted; the tornado season in the Midwest or Southwest, or when one may face major surgery. The time frame involved is usually weeks or months.

Next is the *warning period* or the period of imminent danger. This second phase is usually minutes but may be hours. One often can not estimate time involved in warning. Little information is known about behavior during actual impact, or at least the initial phases of impact. If impact is prolonged, as in combat, one can learn much about behavior, but in brief impact periods, as an explosion or a bombing, individuals can give little data. One may obtain information from subjects, but usually much retrospective addition is included to make the experience conform to standard behavior. Apparently, immediate behavior under sudden impact represents reflex type or relatively primitive responses.

The *recoil period* follows impact. This period may last a varying time, usually minutes, hopefully no longer. It is the period when the individual grasps the situation around him and proceeds in some organized manner to cope with the environment. Finally, there is the *post-impact* phase, a period of weeks or months. It is here that all the sequelae of the disaster occur; it is a time of mourning, repair, and rehabilitation.

PRE-SET PATTERNS

One can readily understand that pre-set patterns of behavior will determine actions during the warning period, which will in turn influence the duration of recoil, which further may be responsible for the existence of sequelae. If an individual's pre-set pattern is such that he is unable to function adequately during warning or recoil promptly and help others, there may be persistent phobic behavior.

PRE-IMPACT PERIOD

Characteristic behavior in pre-impact is usually one of denial, or it may be restlessness, a worried vigilance which if persistent causes ineffective responses upon actual impact. Either type of behavior, denial or restless concern, are usually not effective pre-set patterns. The pre-impact period is the only time phase when one can alter pre-set patterns and thus behavior in the later phases. The warning period is too short and impact circumstances too rapid and uncertain. It is in the pre-impact phase that one must include training for impact, but training for disaster is usually not acceptable. It conjures up repetitions, unpleasurable types of activity, and no one wants to train for his possible destruction. Yet this is the only time phase when one can influence later behavior by the learning process.

REACTIONS TO UNCERTAIN THREAT

The pre-impact phase deals essentially with responses to uncertain threat; dangers which may or may not occur. In such reactions, one faces future but uncertain danger and experiences objective fear, which can be responded to in one of two ways. One response is to become concerned, restless and vigilant, while searching and endeavoring to find out what can be done, or, in effect, exhibiting a form of "fight." On the other hand, one can utilize a mechanism of denial or ascribe one's future to fate and thus respond with "flight." But when the danger is not imminent and one has to deal only with probability, neither of these two pre-set patterns are generally effective. If one fights the uncertain danger, such as the eventualities of combat or diaster, he may overreact to ambiguous stimuli and maintain a high level of tension, which is not conducive to effective behavior when confronted with the actual emergency situation. On the other hand, "flight" is also an ineffective pre-set pattern, since there is little or no preparation for danger. The tendency is to seek information that would help ignore or deny the threat. For example, most individuals successfully deny the possibility of death. Medical students in the third year, in identifying with various illness, develop many symptoms. But in the senior year, they usually assume the doctor's well-known denial mechanism and no longer pay attention to the possibility of incurring disease. Later, as physicians, little concern is paid to their own symptoms, even those of coronary insufficiency. "Flight" is commonly used by almost all persons for minor threats for, indeed, one cannot be concerned and constantly upset with remote threats of little probability. But, for major dangers of high probability, "flight" is unrealistic, for little preparation for the avoidance of and defense against emergency situations is accomplished.

Major threats are also denied by rationalization; for example, cigarette smoking (it has not been proven and there are many other carcinogens in the atmosphere). Prior to World War II, Sinclair Lewis wrote a book entitled *It Can't Happen Here*, which concerned ignoring the Nazi penetration and menace which had developed in the USA. It is common to deny the possibility of nuclear warfare—that it can't happen. "The Russians have the bomb and we have it and it would be mutual suicide." Another form of denial is to utilize fate, "what will be, will be." Thus, when danger occurs, the individual is ill-prepared to cope.

CONTINGENCY RESPONSE

What then is the preferred pre-set behavioral pattern to uncertain danger? The most effective pattern is a *contingency response* mechanism(1). Here, an individual learns when to become concerned, what signals indicate that danger is near. In conventional warfare in rear areas, one can observe much sound and tumult of war. Yet, in this artillery area where there is a great deal of firing, men are walking about, writing letters, playing volleyball, and so forth. To the uninitiated, these men seem quite courageous. But when incoming fire occurs, an immediate change occurs and unconcern is absent. The contingency response is to promptly take cover in previously prepared positions of safety. For example, there was a major explosion in a Texas city years ago at a time of concern with nuclear warfare. It involved a fireworks factory which exploded, following which a large mushroom cloud appeared. Many thought that an atomic attack had occurred. However, there was one person found who knew that it was not a nuclear explosion. He was a former Navy enlisted man who had been at an atomic test site. He knew that the explosion was not due to a nuclear bomb because it was not preceded by a brilliant white flash—the hallmark of a nuclear detonation. The experienced physician also knows when to become concerned or when a patient has a relatively minor problem. Contingency responses are possible when one has knowledge of danger agents and their effects, so that proper steps can be taken upon the existence of relevant signals. The military is well known for training in contingency response. It trains personnel so that the warning period can be utilized adequately so as to place into operation a preconceived plan of action.

WARNING

The warning phase is a period of little time. The word "panic" has often been ascribed to this phase, although true panic behavior seldom occurs. However, much noneffective behavior does occur when there is an absence of a prepared plan or little provision for leadership to improvise an adequate response. A survey of the Worcester tornado disaster found much ineffective behavior during warning period, which carried over in the emergency—even by hospitals in caring for mass casualties.

True panic rarely occurs in outdoor situations. People may flee but have egress and there is no panic. True panic only occurs when escape routes are narrowed or blocked. When individuals are in flight from danger and find their escape blocked, then panic occurs, a type of blind animal-like self-destructive behavior. Most panic occurs in indoor situations, as was the well-known Cocoanut Grove disaster in Boston. Ordinarily, outdoor disaster situations produce flight or stunned behavior. Often the term "panic" has been used loosely to describe flight from alleged danger. The best known example of such behavior was in 1938, due to the Orson Welles radio broadcast of *The War of the Worlds* in which the Martians were landing in New Jersey. The realistic radio program impelled many to leave via automobile to escape the danger. The flight resulted in many accidents but no panic—mainly noneffective flight due to faulty information.

To summarize, the warning phase is a brief time period which usually permits only the implementation of a preconceived plan or effort, e.g. hospitals having an emergency plan.

IMPACT

Behavior in impact period of an explosive type disaster is difficult to determine, as opposed to a prolonged impact period such as a flood or epidemic. For example in combat of World War II it was necessary for S.L.A. Marshall, the military historian, to develop a debriefing technique where one would interview together all the individuals involved soon after the battle in order to obtain accurate data regarding behavior during combat. One comes out of battle with a peculiarly circumscribed viewpoint of the events. For example, combat participants in World War II would insist that they were the last person in their company. Indeed, to them they were the only person remaining, for they could not know the whereabouts of others.

RECOIL

The recoil phase occurs when the individual recovers awareness and physical capability. It may be an important period because of secondary hazards due to collapsing walls, fire, or situations such as the immediate need for rescue of injured. In military situations, it is important to reorganize for defense against enemy attack. A common military strategy is to subject an enemy to heavy artillery barrage to induce a state of delayed recoil so as to permit an offensive attack to proceed with little opposition. So much depends on rapid recoil. If the recoil is delayed, then the assault moves in amongst stunned, dazed defenders who can offer little defense. Recoil is also a significant phase of behavior in civil disaster because many types of secondary danger may confront uninjured survivors. One can consider the behavior in the recoil phase by utilizing the usual bell curve. The ascending arm represents the most effective individuals who promptly after impact were able to grasp the relevant aspects of the situation and to proceed to effective action for self and assume leadership for others. In contrast, the descending arm of the bell curve represents increasing noneffective behavior. The ascending arm includes between 12 to 20 per cent of persons who are able in a relatively short period of time to recoil and function adequately within a brief time period. Students of civil and military emergency situations arrive at similar conclusions. A well-trained, well-led, cohesive group will produce a higher proportion of persons with prompt recoil. A heterogenous group who happen to be involved in an emergency area will have larger numbers of individuals with considerable delayed recoil.

The top or middle of the bell curve which represents about 50 per cent of persons, who apparently have ability to receive information, to understand the emergency situation, but seem unable to take decisive action. Characteristically, they are described as irresolute, docile, or suggestible. A leader can mobilize large numbers of such individuals to effective action. In approximately 20 to 25 per cent of persons in the descending arm of the bell curve who exhibit increasing types of noneffective responses, there are firstly, those individuals who also can receive information but are seemingly helpless to follow orders and need to be pushed, coerced, or led by the hand. Many of this group come to believe that they are helpless by virtue of the disaster agent. For example, during World War I, a rear division was attacked by "gas." Almost promptly there occurred five hundred gas casualties until it was determined that the "gas" was merely the acrid fumes of usual high explosives. The psychiatric diagnosis of World War I, or the so-called shell-shock, came from massive artillery fire to indicate that men were "shocked" by the force of high explosives.

In the second group of descending arm of the bell curve are persons who seem to have withdrawn from the situation. They appear to be mute, stunned, or dazed. These individuals are psychologically withdrawn from the situation. Finally, there are a very small number of extremely noneffective persons, who seem to have lost all ability to organize action and exhibit primitive or reflex type behavior. It is important to note, in all responses, time is the important variable. At the instant of impact one may consider the entire exposed population to be ineffective, but within a few minutes some will have recoiled and move to appropriate action. Within fifteen minutes, a much larger number will be so mobilized. Within hours, most exposed persons have become effective. Dazed individuals have moved into the docile group, to become capable of direction toward effective behavior. If one waits twenty-four hours, there are very few who remain ineffective.

POST-IMPACT

The post-impact phase is a period of recrimination and of sequelae when individuals take stock and fully realize the loss of life and property. At this time, individuals place blame, become concerned about the lack of emergency planning, and often direct their wrath at the formal leaders such as mayor, chief of police, and so on.

During this period, participants of disaster also examined their own behavior, as exemplified by the book *We of Nagasaki*, which traces the action of twelve individual Japanese after the atomic destruction of Nagasaki, who blame themselves for selfish behavior such as not helping others. Other problems are phobias. Much of the so-called combat fatigue represent a sequelae of what had occurred in a previous combat situation. Soldiers developed specific phobic avoidance behavior related to shell fire. In previous combat episodes, they were rendered helpless or failed to cope with the combat situation. In this respect, there was encountered the "old sergeant syndrome." These veterans came from the outstanding men of the unit; usually the last survivors of a company who finally, after repeated combat episodes, reached a point of phobic avoidance of battle. They were sent back by their commanders with glowing accounts of former combat effectiveness, but had become unable to function. Such individuals were placed in noncombat positions. The British found that some of their veteran London firefighters, after months of working under bombing, would develop a similar phobic behavior.

REFERENCE

1. JANIS, IRVING: Chapter 3 in Baker, George W., and Chapman, Dwight W. (Ed.): *Man and Society in Disaster*. New York, Basic Books, 1962.

Chapter 5

PSYCHOLOGICAL ASPECTS OF COMBAT

PETER G. BOURNE

HISTORICAL BACKGROUND

DURING the Civil War, William Hammond, who was Surgeon General of the Union Army, described a condition which he termed "nostalgia," that afflicted the minds of soldiers making them incapable of performing their duties yet without any evidence of physical injury(1). His treatment proposal contains the essential elements that we still recognize today. He wrote

> The best means of preventing nostalgia is to provide occupation for the mind and the body. . . . Soldiers placed in hospitals near their homes are always more liable to nostalgia than those who are inmates of hospitals situated in the midst of or in the vicinity of the Army to which they belong.

The Union Army reported 5,213 cases of nostalgia during the first year of the Civil War and almost twice as many during the second year.

The first time in any army that mental illness in military personnel was treated by specialists in psychiatry was in the Russo-Japanese War of 1904 to 1905. However the Russian psychiatric casualties were so numerous that the service was soon overwhelmed and it became necessary to turn over large numbers of patients to the Red Cross for treatment and disposition(2).

It was not until World War I that the planning for psychiatric casualties became an integral part of the overall medical organization. For the first time also, systematic observations were made on the phenomenon of psychic disintegration in combat, and copious if often inaccurate, speculations were generated as to the possible

70

etiology of the condition. In a war characterized by relentless and heavy artillery bombardment of both sides the reasonable assumption was made that a soldier's brain became chronically concussed by his constant proximity to exploding shells, with multiple petechial hemorrhages occurring in the cerebrum. For this reason the term "shell shock" was coined to describe such cases. The French, however, distinguished between "emotionée," the less severe cases that were felt to occur on an emotional basis, and "commotionée," a term generally reserved for those exhibiting psychotic symptoms and considered to have an organic etiology to their condition(3).

One of the most detailed accounts of the psychological aspects of combat in World War I was made by Lord Moran, in his book, *The Anatomy of Courage*(4). While not a psychiatrist, his sensitivity to the suffering of those in the trenches with him as well as his astute sense of observation made his work a classic in the field. However, even Moran's humanitarian nature did not prevent him from occasionally lapsing into the moralistic stance characteristic of most physicians towards combat psychiatric casualties at that time. He wrote

> There were others who were plainly worthless fellows. One without moral sense had taken a commission under the shadow of compulsion. . . . Sitting there with his head in his hands at the bottom of the trench, he could do no good to the men of 1916. He showed none of the extreme signs of fear, he was just a worthless chap, without shame, the worst product of the towns.

Interestingly, now we would probably more generously classify such a case as a character and behavior disorder.

Many distinguished psychiatrists of the period including Southard, Jones, Kardiner, Ferenczi, and Freud drew upon the military experience of World War I to formulate their explanations of man's response to the stresses of combat and extrapolated from it to explain how comparable traumatic events are dealt with in a civilian setting.

By the time the United States entered the war the psychological aspects of combat stress were better understood, and Dr. Thomas W. Salmon, assigned to direct the psychiatric program in support of the American Expeditionary Force (AEF), was able to benefit from the past experience and failures of both the French and the

British. Both French and British had made the acknowledged mistake of evacuating their psychiatric casualties out of the combat zone. In 1917 Salmon assigned a psychiatrist to each American division with instructions to treat all but the most severe or persistent psychiatric casualties at forward medical facilities, maintaining the expectation that these men would return to combat. So effective was his approach that in the few remaining months prior to the armistice, 65 per cent of the casualties were returned to duty after an average stay of seven days(5).

At the start of World War II military psychiatry in the United States was in marked disarray and poorly prepared to provide organization and staffing of a psychiatric support program for combat operations. There seemed to be little awareness of the hard learned lessons of the previous war, and the treatment program of proven efficacy established by Dr. Salmon was apparently forgotten. Between January 1943 and December 1945 there were 409,887 neuropsychiatric patients admitted to Army hospitals overseas, and 127,660 of these patients were evacuated to the United States(2). At one point early in 1943, psychiatric casualties were occurring at a faster rate than recruits were being drafted into the service(6). The highest rate of neuropsychiatric casualties—101 per thousand troops per year—occurred in the First United States Army in Europe and compared with 37 per thousand per year in Korea and 12 per thousand per year in Viet Nam(7). Much of this attrition might have been avoided had the military been better prepared, and had it not been necessary to relearn with considerable anguish, the lessons of twenty years earlier.

Many distinguished psychiatrists served the military during World War II, and several utilized their talents to apply scientific research methodology to the data they obtained on psychiatric casualties (8, 9). Particularly the work of Grinker and Spiegel described in their book, *Men Under Stress*(10), represented a major advance in the systematic evaluation of man's psychological response to combat. These data assumed particular significance after the war when it became apparent that observations on the adaptation of the individual to the extreme stress of war had significant application to our understanding of civilian stress situations.

Aside from the observations made upon the individual's psychological adaptation to combat, sociologists examined the social organization in which the soldier functioned. They identified the "primary group" as the critical social unit in providing emotional support for the individual(11). Solidarity and intimacy with fellow soldiers on a small group level as well as an intense desire to preserve the group as a social entity was seen as characterizing the social organization in that war.

In Korea, after an initial period of hesitancy an effective program for the treatment of neuropsychiatric casualties was established under the direction of Dr. Albert Glass(12). Salmon's principles of proximity, immediacy, and expectancy, rediscovered in World War II, were further refined. Between 50 and 75 per cent of those diagnosed as "Combat Exhaustion" at the division level or forward were returned to duty. Col. Donald B. Peterson, who replaced Glass as Far East Command Consultant in October 1951, demonstrated a drop in the ratio of neurotic to psychotic evacuees from the theater between the last quarter of 1950 to the first half of 1951 from 19.4:1 to 3.6:1. This ratio further dropped as the psychiatric services developed, to 1:5.4 in 1952 and 1:9.3 in 1953(13).

For the first time in Korea investigators entered the war zone expressly to study the effects of combat stress on man. Under the direction of Dr. David Rioch of Walter Reed Army Institute of Research, a systematic assessment was made of the soldier's response to combat both as an individual and as a member of an organizational unit. The field study team headed by Major F. Gentry Harris concerned itself not only with men who became casualties but also with the method by which the overwhelming majority of soldiers coped with the stress of the environment without psychological disintegration(14). Harris found that whereas in World War II the "primary group" provided critical emotional support for the soldier, in Korea the diadic relationship of the "buddy system" performed this function.

In addition to psychological responses to stress, for the first time an attempt was made to measure the physiological correlates of psychic adaptation. Hampered to some extent by logistical problems and the limited assay methods of that cra, a multidisciplinary team collected blood and urine samples from men in combat to measure altered excretion of 17-ketosteroids(15).

With the advent of the Viet Nam War the military was well prepared to handle large numbers of psychiatric casualties with all the experience and expertise gained from three previous wars. There was every reason to believe that the number of psychiatric casualties would be high. The physically demanding conditions of jungle warfare, the ubiquitous enemy, and the absence of established battle lines, plus the political controversy surrounding the war, all suggested that the stress on the individual G.I. would be considerable. However the effects of these factors, if any, have not been felt in terms of the number of psychiatric casualtes.

The incidence of psychiatric problems requiring hospitalization has remained about the same as that for a comparable stateside force. Many of those seen by psychiatrists in Viet Nam have problems unrelated to the direct stresses of war, and indeed the bulk of cases come from support units rather than those actually engaged in combat. In World War II psychiatric casualties were common occurrences in fighter and bomber pilots(16), while in Viet Nam the problem has been virtually nonexistent. Six per cent of all medical evacuations from Viet Nam are for psychiatric reasons as compared with 23 per cent in World War II. Only approximately 5 per cent of psychiatric admissions have been diagnosed as having "combat fatigue," while 40 per cent or higher are classified as character and behavior disorders(17).

The reasons why the incidence of psychiatric casualties should vary so widely from one war to another and why one individual should succumb to the psychological stresses of combat while another survives are considered below.

CLINICAL PATTERNS AND FACTORS RELATING TO INCIDENCE

Beginning with the term "nostalgia," acute psychological breakdown in combat has since been variously labeled "shell shock," "traumatic neurosis of war," "combat exhaustion," and "combat fatigue." Clinically it is a polymorphous entity varying from acute psychotic states to conversion reactions with hysterical blindness, deafness, paralytic phenomena, and myoclonus. At times there may be disturbances in orientation varying from temporary confusion to total amnesia and often signs of sympathetic nervous system overstimulation including dilation of the pupils, slightly proptosed eyes, and tachycardia. Crying, uncontrolled fear, and protective overreaction such as "ducking" and covering the head in response to the slightest unexpected sound. The development of such symptom patterns in association with exposure to combat form the basis for a diagnosis of combat fatigue.

What are the factors which contribute to the development of combat fatigue? Clearly, and essentially by definition, exposure to combat is the primary factor. Appel(18) cites an admission rate to overseas hospitals for neuropsychiatric conditions in 1944 of 47.0 per 1000 mean troop strength, while the admission rate for combat divisions was approximately 250 per 1000 mean troop strength. Tompkins(19) demonstrated a significant relationship between actual danger and the incidence of neurosis among combat fliers. Utilizing the number of wounded in action as a measure of the intensity of combat, Glass(20) and Appel(18) demonstrated a correlation between psychiatric attrition and the intensity of combat.

Nonbattle factors also contribute significantly to the incidence of psychiatric casualties. Menninger(21) identified isolation, boredom, inadequte diet, chronic physical discomfort, exhaustion, and physical illness as contributing to a high incidence of psychiatric casualties in relatively low hazard situations. Appel(18) reported that the effects of privation increase with time, stating that men who had been in the service for more than eighteen months lost more man days due to illness than those in for less than eighteen months. Time is an equally important variable in hazardous conditions. Glass(20) and Appel(18) cite data which demonstrates a correlation between the total number of days of combat exposure and psychological breakdown. After eighty to one hundred days of combat exposure the psychological vulnerability of the soldier increases sharply with a probability that his performance will decline significantly.

Conflicting data exists as to whether preexisting psychological conditions are a contributing factor to psychiatric attrition in a combat zone. Hastings(16) reported that in his series of fliers who failed under minimal stress there was no evidence of predisposing neurotic illness. On the other hand Brill and Beebe(22) found that men with preexisting neuroses had seven to eight times the probability of developing overt symptomatology and behavioral disorders as compared with previously well-integrated individuals. In studying a series of one hundred and fifty men who successfully completed their tours in the combat zone Grinker and Spiegel(10) found that one half had a previous life pattern of emotional instability. Overall it may be stated that individuals with preexisting emotional problems or demonstrated maladjustment in school, work, or family relationships are more likely to be vulnerable to other factors which correlate with psychological breakdown in the combat zone.

All other factors being equal, it has been demonstrated that the incidence of psychiatric casualties varies considerably from one unit to another. This is attributable to an aggregate of forces which are collectively described as morale. While morale remains difficult to define in specific terms, it may be considered to refer to the general sense of well-being enjoyed by the group and to be a reflection of confidence in their ability to successfully survive environmental stresses, faith in the quality of their leadership and an overall sense of cooperation and cohesiveness among the members. The importance of leadership in maintaining moral has been demonstrated by Appel(18), who showed that there was a correlation between the number of men evacuated from each infantry company of the same division engaged in heavy combat and the number of leaders evacuated from those same companies. Grinker and Spiegel(10) emphasized the importance of group cohesiveness and esprit in functioning as a mitigating factor against psychological attrition.

There is ample evidence to substantiate the belief that morale serves as an important emotional force in a unit providing group support and mutual reinforcement which reduces the vulnerability to psychological breakdown. There is also evidence that it correlates with lowered physical casualty rates, even in noncombat situations(23).

While the major emphasis in determining correlates of psychological attrition in combat has focused on the soldier under fire, there is reason to believe that the quality of combat itself is an important determinant. Neuropsychiatric casualties in combat occur predominantly when the lines of battle are static and diminish sharply when the troops are on the move even though they may be in full retreat. It is also accepted that artillery or other bombardment without any effective method of retaliation is more likely to produce psychiatric casualties than any other combat circumstance.

CURRENT CONCEPTS AND THE WAR IN VIET NAM

During World War I combat exhaustion was considered largely a time-determined phenomenon and it was assumed that once a man "broke" he was lost for good from the battlefield. As a result the belief existed among line officers that the men should be pushed hard in order to obtain a maximal performance from them before they were irretrievably lost as psychiatric casualties. We now know that combat exhaustion is not a progressive phenomenon, but more a dynamic state influenced by a variety of external and constitutional forces and is quite reversible at any point in its development. In the past it was similarly assumed that the overwhelming concern for the soldier was the fear of death or mutilation in combat and that this stress alone constituted the etiology of psychiatric casualties. It is now appreciated that the possibility of death may represent a relatively minor stress to the soldier, provided adequate opportunity exists for him to adapt to it.

Combat may be viewed as a situation bearing many similarities to other life circumstances, to which man is capable of making a satisfactory emotional and behavioral adaptation. Studies conducted in Viet Nam have supported the view that a state of psychological and even physiological homeostasis can be maintained despite repeated exposure to objectively high risk situations. In studies which we conducted on helicopter ambulance crews and a Special Forces "A" team, it was apparent that our subjects used extensive and effective psychological defenses to handle the threat of death or injury to which they were exposed(24, 25). One subject was a sincerely religious Catholic who believed that God would protect him no matter how great the danger. This feeling was considerably reinforced by his successful survival throughout the Korean War, during which he was exposed to even more hazardous conditions. A second subject had carefully calculated from the number of flights he flew, the number of casualties in the unit during the previous year, and the length of his tour in Viet Nam, a statistical estimate of the probability of his being killed or injured on any given day. The chance was reassuringly small. Other men, particularly those in Special Forces, were independent, self-reliant individuals with inordinate faith in their own abilities and a sense of omnipotence which they used to deny the possibility that they might be killed. All of the subjects, using a wide range of defenses, were able to psychologically restructure their perception of reality in such a way that they avoided facing the danger and at the same time enhanced their own sense of immortality and invulnerability.

This mechanism was succinctly described a number of years ago by Sandor Rado(26). He stated that

> By far the most efficient technique at the soldier's disposal in re-solving this conflict is completely to ignore the dangers surrounding him as though disregarding his own life, and stop the entire working of emergency control. Transformed from a sensitive man into an in-sensitive technician of war, he then interprets combat not as a con-tinued threat of injury but as a sequence of operational demands to be responded to by precise military performances.

The profound effectiveness of this adaptational maneuver at even a physiological level is reflected by the finding of urinary 17-hy-droxycorticosteroid levels in our subjects that were normal or even lower than normal supporting the belief that there is a generalized suppression of affective arousal(24).

While successful adaptation of this sort characterizes the combat experience of the overwhelming majority of soldiers, there remain those whose adaptive capacity fails them. Prolonged exposure to combat, very traumatic or horrifying experiences, as well as an ag-gregate of the factors described in the previous section which in-crease psychological vulnerability can open flaws in the defensive wall the soldier has built up around himself. Confronted with the deaths of friends and "near miss" situations where he himself nar-rowly survives, some soldiers can eventually no longer deny that combat is dangerous and ominously lethal. At this point there is an increasing tendency to fall back on the belief that while others may get killed he himself is somehow immune and will survive. Without relief the man will begin to develop increasing doubts about his own ability to survive and at this point is likely to develop overt and in-capacitating symptoms.

The question of individual difference in a man's ability to successfully adapt to combat is obviously raised. The equivocal evidence from previous wars concerning the importance of preexisting psychopathology has been touched on above. However, data from Viet Nam on this issue appears more conclusive. In an analysis of Marine and Navy neuropsychiatric casualties hospitalized on the ship *Repose*, Strange(27) found that individuals with a history of difficulty adapting to society prior to enlistment were more likely to fail to adapt in a combat situation. He divided combat precipitated psychiatric syndromes into three categories—combat fatigue, pseudocombat fatigue, and combat neurosis.

Combat fatigue comprised 15 per cent of his overall patient group. These men were characterized by good premorbid adjustment, exposure to extreme stress coupled with other privation, rapid improvement with treatment, and generally successful return to duty. They tended to be young men with positions of considerable responsibility as squad leaders or hospital corpsmen working with combat units. This observation is consistent with the finding of elevated steroid levels in certain unit commanders(25).

Pseudocombat fatigue comprised the majority of his patients. These individuals presented similar clinical pictures to those in the first group but were distinct in that most had been in Viet Nam less than six months, the combat conditions to which they had been exposed were less severe, and they characteristically had past histories of difficulties in impulse control as well as in social, family, and school relationships. They rarely had been in positions of responsibility in combat and their recoveries were slower, with frequent exacerbations of their symptoms at the prospect of returning to duty.

Combat neurosis comprised a smaller group than those with pseudocombat fatigue. These were men with histories of long standing neurotic problems that were aggravated by the stresses of combat. While these men required longer periods of hospitalization, their prognosis was substantially better than for those with pseudocombat fatigue, and their return to duty rate approached that for those in the first category of combat fatigue.

While the overall incidence of neuropsychiatric casualties and particularly combat fatigue in Viet Nam has remained low, the diagnosis of character and behavior disorders has consistently led other categories in both inpatient and outpatient statistics(28-30). In a series of two hundred enlisted men referred for evaluation to an evacuation hospital in Viet Nam, Tischler(31) found that only 13 per cent were classified as psychotic or neurotic. However, while the majority of his patients carried the label of character and behavior disorder, an extensive analysis of his data revealed an extremely interesting correlation between the patient's premorbid adjustment, his age, marital status, and military experience and the point in time during his one-year tour that he was referred to the psychiatric service. Approximately one half of the men referred for evaluation had been in Viet Nam for less than four months. The number of referrals dropped markedly after the third month and remained at a consistent but diminished level from the fourth to the ninth month. During the last three months a second progressive decrease occurred, with only 2 per cent of the patients seen being in the last month of their tour. The men referred during the first three months of their tour were characteristically between the ages of seventeen and twenty, came from nuclear families that were intact, their relationships with their parents were positive, over half had completed high school, and most were single. In addition they tended to have less than three years service, to be of the rank of Private First Class, and to have service records significantly better than men referred later in their tours. Arrival in Viet Nam produces enormous anxiety and a sense of helplessness generated both by cultural shock and the uncertainty of the combat zone. Tischler has identified three patterns of behavior by which most of the soldiers cope with the threatening uncertainty of their new environment: (1) fusion with the group, (2) a search for an authority figure to provide order and security for the group, and (3) a flight into work. Those referred for psychiatric evaluation at this early stage proved to be individuals who for some personal and often idiosyncratic reason were unable to avail themselves of any of these ways of attenuating their anxiety. Many of these individuals came to the attention of the authorities because the methods by which they attempted to resolve their discomfort deviated too markedly from these three normative patterns of behavior.

Patients seen between the fourth and ninth month appeared to come from a different population. They were older, being mostly over twenty-one, single, and white. Like the previous group they also tended to be from intact families and to have positive relationships with their parents. However, unlike the first group they had generally achieved the rank of E-3 or higher and their military records were significantly poorer, with higher incidences of AWOL, article fifteens, and court martials. Most men in Viet Nam are able to accept the danger and privations of combat and compensate for it by accentuating their indulgence in the pleasures that are available to them. There is an inordinate acquisition of material goods such as cameras, hi-fi sets, and tape recorders. Bars, brothels, and particularly R & R (rest and recuperation) provide programmed escape from the reality of combat in which the soldier feels justified in immersing himself to balance the hardship of his duty time. Tischler has labeled this pattern of compensatory overindulgence as the hedonistic pseudocommunity. He noted that the group of patients that he saw between the fourth and ninth month tended to be individuals who had difficulty balancing tolerance of the suffering of combat with an appropriate period of pleasurable gratification. Many of these men, often after very traumatic experiences in battle, fled into hedonism as a permanent method of escape, making return to combat intolerable.

The final group which he described are those who were seen during the last three months of their tour. As a group they again appeared to be drawn from a distinct segment of the military population in Viet Nam. They could be characterized as coming from disrupted nuclear families, as having negative relationships with their parents, and while the majority were married, 57 per cent had not received letters from home during their tour. Thirty-six per cent had not graduated from high school, and although they were older and had achieved the rank of E-4 or higher, they had service records that were extremely poor, with 36 per cent having been AWOL, 60 per cent having had Article Fifteens, and 40 per cent having been court martialed at least once. A clear relationship existed between role failure and psychiatric attrition during the last three months of the tour. While most of the men in Viet Nam look forward with excitement to their return to the United States and eagerly anticipate what the future will hold for them, this group of patients have only the repetition of past failures to look forward to. In addition, for many of these men the tour in Viet Nam had provided a measure of gratification, and not only had they been absolved from stateside responsibility, but they had formed strong personal bonds with their comrades. For these men service in the combat zone had provided a certain opportunity for adaptive success and reentry into the United States represented a greater threat than remaining in Viet Nam.

The low incidence of psychiatric attrition in Viet Nam has been attributed to the rigorous implementation of preventive measures based on the insights gained in previous wars(6). Of these planned measures the one-year tour (thirteen months for Marines) is generally credited with having the most profound effect. However, a study by Moskos(32) shows that aside from lowering the incidence of psychiatric casualties it has had a significant influence on the total social behavior in the war zone. For most of the men who go to Viet Nam, their entire conceptualization of the war and their personal involvement in it revolves around this issue. The war becomes a highly individualized and encapsulated event for each man. His war begins the day he arrives in Viet Nam and ends the day he leaves. He feels no continuity with those who precede or follow him; he even feels apart from those who are with him but rotating on a different schedule. The universal objective, barring death or injury, is the personal DEROS—Date Expected to Return from Overseas—a day known exactly to each man from the moment he arrives in Viet Nam.

Aside from the emotional effects on the individual, the staggered arrivals and departures necessitated by the rotation system break down the traditional solidarity of the small unit. There is little evidence in Viet Nam of either the "primary group," identified in World War II, or the "buddy system" of Korea as important social structures to provide a source for dependence and emotional support. Emotional independence in the combat zone in Viet Nam is greatly facilitated by the possibility of phone calls to the United States and by the relative excellence of the mail service. The feasibility of maintaining the continuity with preexisting emotional ties in this country and the knowledge that they can be reintensified at a predictable point within the next year reduces the need to seek gratification from sentimental attachments to those in the immediate and temporary environment.

The time limitation imposed by the one-year tour guarantees the G. I. that if he can merely survive for twelve months his removal from combat is assured. There is not the sense of hopelessness that has prevailed in previous wars where death, injury, or peace were the only possible ways in which the soldier could find himself extricated from combat. This has contributed immeasurably to maintaining high morale and in turn has helped to lower the rate of psychiatric casualties.

The Viet Nam experience has enhanced in many respects our understanding of the psychology of combat and secondarily our ability to provide psychiatric service in time of war. It has been shown that we have now successfully identified most of the major correlates of psychiatric attrition in the combat zone and that we have been able to incorporate into our conduct of the war many measures based on this knowledge that have significantly reduced the psychological vulnerability of the average fighting man to combat stress. It is also now demonstrated that when attention is paid to providing the support that enhances the adaptive capacity of the soldier he is able to make a highly successful adaptation to combat at both a psychological and physiological level. It is then only under very unusual circumstances, when combat is extremely heavy or when he becomes excessively tired, that a healthly man will become a psychiatric casualty, and when he does, prompt appropriate treatment will rapidly reestablish his capacity to cope with his environment so that he can return to duty. Significant psychiatric attrition has been in Viet Nam and presumably will be in the future, largely confined to those who bring some psychological liability with them to the combat zone. However, even with this group diligent attention to the proven preventative measures that enhance successful adaptation will minimize the incidence of psychiatric casualties. Our level of knowledge of combat psychology has now reached a point where with adequate vigilence psychiatric casualties need never again become a major cause of attrition in the United States military in a combat zone.

REFERENCES

1. HAMMOND, W.A.: *A Treatise on Insanity in Its Medical Relations.* London, H.K. Lewis, 1883.
2. ANDERSON, R.S.: *Neuropsychiatry in World War II.* Washington, D.C., Office of the Surgeon General, 1966, Vol. I.
3. HAUSMAN, W., and RIOCH, D.: Military psychiatry. *Arch Gen Psychiat XVI*:727-739, 1967.
4. MORAN, LORD: *The Anatomy of Courage.* London, Constable, 1945.
5. SALMON, T.W.: The war neurosis and their lesson. New York, *J Med CIX*:993-994, 1919.
6. TIFFANY, W.J., and ALLERTON, W.S.: Army psychiatry in the mid-60's. *Amer J Psychiat, CXXIII*:810-821, 1967.
7. *Fact Sheet.* Washington, D.C., United States Army Surgeon General's Office, February 1967.
8. Combat psychiatry. *Bull US Army Med Dept* (Suppl.), November 1949.
9. GLASS, A.J.: Effectiveness of forward neuropsychiatric treatment. *Bull US Army Med Dept, VII*:1034-1041, 1947.
10. GRINKER, R.R., and SPIEGEL, J.P.: *Men Under Stress.* New York, McGraw-Hill, 1963.
11. SHILS, E.A.: Primary groups in the American army. In Lazarfeld, P.F. (Ed.): *Continuities in Social Research: Studies in the Scope and Method of the American Soldier.* Glencoe, Free Press, 1950.
12. GLASS, A.J.: Psychiatry in the Korean campaign. *US Armed Forces Med J, IV* (parts I and II):1387-1401, 1563-1583, 1954.
13. PETERSON, D.B.: The psychiatric operation Armed Forces Far East, 1950-1953. *Amer J Psychiat, CXII*:23-38, 1955.
14. HARRIS, F.G.; MAYER, J., and BECKER, H.A.: *Experineces in the Study of Combat in the Korean Theater: I. Report on Psychiatric and Psychological Data.* Washington, D.C., Walter Reed Army Institute of Research, WRAIR-43-55, 1955.
15. ELMADJIAN, F.: Adrenocortical function of combat infantry men in Korea. *Ciba Cologuium-Endocrinology, VIII*:627-655, 1955.
16. HASTINGS, D.W.; WRIGHT, D.G., and GLUECK, B.C.: *Psychiatric Experience of the Eighth Air Force, First Year of Combat (July 4, 1942-July 4, 1943).* New York, Josiah Macy, Jr., Foundation, 1944.
17. BOURNE, P.G., and SAN, N.D.: A comparative study of neuropsychiatric casualties in the United States Army and the Army of the Republic of Viet Nam. *Milit Med, CXXXII*:904-909, 1967.
18. APPEL, J.W.: In Anderson, R.S.; Glass, A.J., and Bernucci, R.J. (Eds.): *Neuropsychiatry in World War II.* Washington, D.C., Office of the Surgeon General, 1966, Vol. I.
19. TOMPKINS, V.H.: In Hambling, J. (Ed.): *The Nature of Stress Disorder.* Springfield, Charles C Thomas, 1959.
20. GLASS, A.J.: Observations upon the epidemiology of mental illness in

troops during warfare. In *Symposium on Preventive and Social Psychiatry*. Washington, D.C., Walter Reed Army Institute of Research, 1958.

21. MENNINGER, W.C.: *Psychiatry in a Troubled World*. New York, Macmillan, 1948.
22. BRILL, N.Q., and BEEBE, B.W.: *A Follow Up Study of War Neuroses*. Veterans' Administration Medical Monograph. Washington, D.C., United States Government Printing Office, 1955.
23. STOUFFER, S.A.: *The American Soldier*, vol. I and II. Princeton, Princeton University Press, 1949.
24. BOURNE, P.G.; ROSE, R.M., and MASON, J.W.: Urinary 17-OHCS levels. *Arch Gen Psychiat, XVII*:104-110, 1967.
25. BOURNE, P.G.; ROSE, R.M., and MASON, J.W.: Urinary 17-OHCS levels in combat. *Arch Gen Psychiat, XIX*:135-140, 1968.
26. RADO, S.: Pathodynamics and treatment of traumatic war neurosis (traumatophobia). *Psychosom Med, XLIII*:362-368, 1943.
27. STRANGE, R.E.: Effects of combat stress on hospital ship psychiatric evacuees. In Bourne, P.G. (Ed.): *Psychology and Physiology of Stress*. New York, Academic Press, 1969.
28. STRANGE, R.E., and ARTHUR, R.J.: Hospital ship psychiatry in a war zone. *Amer J Psychiat, CXXIV*:37-42, 1967.
29. BYRDY, H.S., and HUFFMAN, E.: Personal communication.
30. BOURNE, P.G.: *Men, Stress, and Viet Nam*. Boston, Little, Brown and Co., 1970.
31. TISCHLER, G.L.: Patterns of psychiatric attrition and of behavior in a combat zone. In Bourne, P.G. (Ed.): *Psychology and Physiology of Stress*. New York, Academic Press, 1969.
32. MOSKOS, C.C.: The American Soldier in Combat. In Moskos, C.C. (Ed.): *The American Enlisted Man*. New York, Russell Sage Foundation, 1969.

Chapter 6

PSYCHOLOGICAL REACTIONS
TO THE STRESSES OF OUTER SPACE

E. J. McLAUGHLIN

SEVERAL years ago our office conducted a study to identify the stresses which might be encountered by astronauts in manned space flight. Table 6-1 is a listing of those stresses. We can consider this list as representative of the "nominal" stresses which might be expected in manned flight and use this listing as a point of departure for this presentation.

TABLE 6-1

LIST OF ENVIRONMENTAL STRESSES

Weightlessness	Particulate Matter
Radiation	Microorganisms
Confinement	Change in Circadian Rhythms
Social Isolation	Magnetic Fields
Monotony	Ultraviolet Exposure
Threat of Danger	Infrared Exposure
Artificial Atmosphere	Noise
Toxic Substances	

Some of these conditions could be expected to elicit psychological responses. Others would elicit primarily physiological responses. All could elicit psychophysiological reactions. I have attempted to identify those stresses, the response to which could have a major psychological component.

I find that I am required to initiate this presentation with a conclusion; namely, that the twenty-three flight crew members who have participated in approximately 4,500 hours of United States manned space flight have responded psychologically in a most adequate manner. That is to say that there have been no unusual or untoward psychological responses to space flight. This is not to say that there have been no strong emotional responses; but I do mean to state that such responses, when they did occur, appeared entirely appropriate to the man and the situation.

Let us discuss each of these stress situations. There are some which we can consider together and dismiss rather quickly inasmuch as the levels encountered were below threshold limits which might be expected to elicit responses. I would group here radiation, artificial atmospheres, toxic substances, and noise. The maximum radiation level measured on any mission was less than 5 rads—and a good deal less on most of the other missions. The prime response to excessive radiation is primarily physiological—skin reaction or hematological effects. I have included it on our list only because at very high, acute doses a type of apathy or fatigue has been described in the literature. We have encountered no response, physiological or psychological, to radiation in manned space flight.

We validated the acceptability of a 5 pounds per square inch (psi) pure oxygen atmosphere in fairly extensive ground-based studies which reached thirty days in duration. We have been able to maintain this 5 psi pressure in manned space flight and have flown for a maximum of fourteen days. We have encountered no psychological responses to our selected artificial atmosphere.

We have set a limit of 7 mm of Hg as the maximum acceptable limit for carbon dioxide. Fortunately, this level, set far below the threshold for psychophysiological responses, has never been exceeded during any of our missions.

I am unable to relate to you the levels of ambient noise encountered in the cabin; however, I feel certain that it has been less than that established as our specification. It is interesting, however, to note that on recent missions the cabin fans have been reported as "noisy and bothersome" and the crew has frequently turned the fans off. It was reported that cabin temperature was adequate without the fans, and one crew recommended that the fans be deleted from future flights.

Let us consider monotony and with it "reduced sensory input." I would like to disagree with people who claim that either of these conditions have existed in manned space flight to date. An examination of any mission timeline convinces me that flight crews are busy—and busy with a variety of activities. If we have had a consistent comment throughout our programs, it has been that the crews do not have time to complete all of the activities scheduled for them—and the tasks finally included in the mission plan represent only a fraction of activities which people would desire to see programmed. All of the disciplines have tasks which they would like scheduled—biomedical, earth resources, engineering, technological, and so forth. As an example, the Apollo Applications Program experiment list originally contained over seventy proposed experiments, and we will probably be able to accommodate only about one half of that number in the five flights currently scheduled.

I will agree that sensory stimulation is modified from that on the ground; however, I do question if it is reduced. Obviously kinesthetic inputs derived from physical activities which counteract gravity on earth are lessened, but the mass of information presented both visually and orally to the crew keeps the sensory level at a high pitch. From reports of the "nominal" dehydrated food, I would have to agree that the sense of taste is challenged somewhat less than it is on the ground.

Confinement, and the response to it, is most interesting. To treat this stress most completely, I feel that we should also consider social isolation in concert with confinement. We had but 47 cubic feet of free volume available to the Mercury astronauts. The Mercury flights were single crewman missions and ranged from fifteen minutes in MR-3 to thirty-four hours in MA-9. The two-man Gemini flights ranged to fourteen days in duration and within the Gemini capsule we had only 78 cubic feet available, or 39 cubic feet per crewman. I think the space in the Gemini capsule can be best envisioned by comparing it to the front seat of a Volkswagon, but with no back seat. The Apollo cabin has 366 cubic feet of volume available, or about 120 cubic feet per crewman. It is in Apollo that the crew can finally make significant whole body movements within the cabin. In the flights to date, we have noted no evidence of an unusual response to the confinement and social isolation situations. Some crewmen have expressed annoyance—more frequently with ground contact than with each other—and these expressions have seemed to be consistent with the general reaction pattern of the individual and with the situation. I believe the Gemini

7 crew, the fourteen-day mission, stated they experienced some annoyance—but then how would any person react after fourteen days with the same other person in the front seat of a Volkswagon! There has been no evidence of the "break-away" phenomenon which has been described as experienced by pilots on long duration aircraft missions.

We are concerned about the social isolation type of question. It was for this reason primarily that we in NASA participated in the recently completed Tektite Project. Tektite was a sixty-day undersea mission with four trained marine scientists submerged, in a saturated condition, and engaged in meaningful scientific investigations. You are probably aware that the mission was successfully completed in April 1969; and while we have not had an opportunity to review the behavioral data, we are assured that the crew interacted very adequately and were able to carry out their planned marine science investigations. I'm sure we will see reports in the literature of this study in the near future.

The always present condition once orbit insertion is reached is weightlessness. We have heard and read of dire predictions of what could happen to man, both physiologically and psychologically, once he was exposed to this state. Happily none of these extraordinary reactions have occurred. We have noted some changes, primarily physiological, but little, if any, psychological reactions. Some crewmen have reported a sensation *as if* they were upside down and accompanied by a full feeling in the head. No astronaut experienced disorientation. Generally, weightlessness has produced a pleasant state wherein crewmen have found movements easy to accomplish and pleasant in nature. We have no evidence of "overshooting" in reaching or touching. Weightlessness has proven bothersome in that we have not yet designed some systems adequately so that waste and food management leave much to be desired. The problem is not weightlessness but our inability to compensate for it by appropriate system design.

The conventional earth day/night cycle is altered significantly during space flight. In earth orbital missions the approximate ninety-minute time per revolution is divided equally between light and dark. On the Apollo 8 and 10 missions the spacecraft spent most of their time in sunlight with lunar orbits requiring two hours—again equally split between light and dark. We have been unable to conduct any formal systematic studies of physiological responses to these altered durinal cycles; however, as well as we can determine, crew efficiency has been maintained overall for these varying conditions.

The crews have had some difficulty in establishing adequate sleep cycles, especially early in the mission. To some degree, difficulty with sleep has been related to noise and the movements and activities of the on-duty crewman. To alleviate this problem, we have done two things primarily; first, we have established Cape time as a reference and tried to arrange sleep schedules to coincide with Cape night and day. Secondly, we have established concurrent sleep periods for all crewmen—so that the sleeping astronauts would not be bothered by someone awake and moving about the spacecraft. Both of these procedures have been effective in aiding the crews to gain more satisfying sleep. The Apollo 8 crew attempted a staggered sleep schedule with nearly a full day's activities, without sleep, planned during lunar orbit. This plan resulted in crew fatigue and a decision by the command pilot to suspend much of the planned activity and to introduce sleep periods for the crew. Some crew procedural errors, minor in character, were encountered during this fatigue period. This experience has led to a reevaluation of the timeline planning for subsequent missions. One interesting question was whether we should plan for a sleep period immediately after the lunar landing and the postlanding check-out of the lunar module. Logical reasoning indicated that a five-hour sleep period at this point in the mission would enable the crews to carry out mission planning—either lunar abort or lunar exploration—more efficiently; however, we had to ask the question, Can we expect men to sleep almost immediately after such a feat as being the first humans to land on the moon?

Space flight is a fairly high risk type of activity. Despite the reliability studies, the redundancy in systems, the exhaustive training, and the rest; the multitude of systems and components, the magnitude of power, and the complexity of the operations still identify the high risk aspect of manned space flight. The crews have faced these circumstances most adequately. During the Apollo 9 mission the heart rate of one of the crewmen was reported to be 66 beats per minute! More importantly, two are specific examples. You will recall that during the Gemini 6 launch, the engines shut-down just prior to lift-off. The two crewmen sat atop a live launch vehicle while the ground crews deactivated the Titan. Another instance was that encountered during the Gemini 8 mission. The Gemini capsule, while docked to the Agena, suddenly rotated at a rate of 50 rpm. The crew disengaged the capsule from the docked Agena and effected an emergency landing. We have conducted six extra-vehicular activity operations thus far. We have experienced some thermal problems, in terms of overheating in the space suit and some inability to complete all EVA objectives; however, the problems appear related to equipment design and to lack of training experiences rather than to any psychological response of the crewmen.

These have been the responses of the astronauts who have participated in the United States manned space flight program. I wish to emphasize that I do not wish to generalize from these responses to indicate that these would have been the reactions of you and me. I believe that we in NASA have been most fortunate in our selection and training programs. First, the candidate requirements are quite stringent. I believe that anyone who has qualified for selection, let alone been selected, has been required to demonstrate unusually strong capabilities. By virtue of the fact that they have demonstrated a high degree of capability in engineering and more recently with the selection of astronaut scientists, in the area of science, they come to the program with documented professional accomplishments. This type of success is usually accompanied by demonstrated and acknowledged maturity. In addition, people reach this level of accomplishment only after a proven period of personal discipline. I believe this latter quality is especially manifested in individuals who come to NASA with highly successful careers in the military.

As we proceed with long duration flights and missions with different objectives—missions which focus on scientific investigations rather than primarily engineering accomplishments—we must face the question of adjustment to space of individuals who will be less like the type of astronauts which I have described and more like you and me. While we cannot eliminate many of the stress conditions which have been listed, we are attempting to upgrade our systems to provide greater support to our scientist observers. In the

Apollo Applications Program, for example, we will provide a series of modules designed much more toward meeting human needs than we have seen thus far. An Orbital Workshop will provide living and working space and accommodations far in excess of that which we have thus far been able to attain. We will provide private sleeping quarters for each of the crewmen with individual locker and stowage compartments. We plan on a food management station to increase feeding facilities and an upgrading of the food itself. We have designed a waste management compartment and are working toward final design of the waste management system to approach our earth borne experiences. We hope to provide, on an experimental basis, a whole body cleansing device—perhaps a shower or even a "space bathtub"—which will introduce personal hygiene practices which we have not even approached as yet in space. The experiment work area will include approximately 1250 cubic feet for the conduct of experiments—primarily biomedical—during these long duration missions. The Apollo Telescope Mount is a special module designed specifically, with controls and displays, for viewing and recording the activity of the sun.

With the advancement of systems and crew accommodations, we hope to reduce the stresses of manned space flight to the degree that we may never really know the psychological responses of a typical individual to the rigors of space flight as we know them today.

NAME INDEX

Abram, Harry S., vii
Appel, J. W., 75, 76, 84

Barker, J. C., 24, 26
Beebe, B. W., 75, 85
Bender, H., 21, 26
Bettelheim, Bruno, 54, 61
Bourne, Peter G., v, 70-85
Brill, N. Q., 75, 85
Broad, C. D., 11, 26
Browne, Ivor W., 30, 43

Carington, W., 7, 26
Cassem, N. H., v, 29-43
Chodoff, Paul, v, 44-61
Cohen, Elie A., 54, 61
Cox, W. E., 22, 26

Dann, Sophie, 57, 61
Druss, R. G., 38, 43
Dunham, Nancy, vii

Eisenbud, J., 13, 26, 27

Frankl, Viktor E., 45, 54, 60, 61
Freud, Anna, 57, 60, 61, 71

Glass, Albert J., v, 26-69, 73, 75, 84
Green, C., 5, 14, 27
Grinker, R. R., 72, 76, 84

Hackett, Thomas P., v, 29- 43
Hammond, William A., 70, 84
Harris, Major F. Gentry, 73, 84
Hastings, D. W., 75, 84

Kornfeld, D. S., 38, 43

Lewis, Sinclair, 64-65
Lifton, Robert, 58, 60, 61

Marshall, S. L. A., 66
McLaughlin, E. J., v, 86-92
Menninger, W. C., 75, 85
Moran, Lord, 71, 84
Morris, Robert, Sr., 10
Moskos, C. C., 82, 85

Nicol, J. F., 5

Paine, Albert Bigelow, 4
Peterson, Col. Donald B., 73
Preminger, Otto, 51

Rado, Sandor, 78, 85
Rhine, L. E., 14, 15, 16, 27
Rioch, David, 73
Roll, W. G., 13, 27
Royce, J., 5

Salmon, Thomas W., 71, 72, 73
Saltmarsh, H. F., 5
Sannwald, G., 14, 18, 19, 28
Sidgwick, E. M., 5
Soal, S. G., 7-8, 28
Spiegel, J. P., 72, 76, 84
Sterba, Edith, 57, 61
Stevenson, Ian, v, 3-28
Strange, R. E., 79, 85

Tanagras, A., 13, 28
Taylor, A. P. J., 44
Tenhaeff, W. H. C., 21, 28
Tischler, G. L., 80-81, 85
Tompkins, V. H., 75, 84

Welles, Orson, 66
Wishnie, Howard A., 34, 43

SUBJECT INDEX

P

Panic, emergency reaction, 65-66
Parapsychology, 7-8, 10-11, 13, 25
Patients
  cardiac arrest survival, 38-39
  defense mechanisms, 40-41
  intensive care reaction, 35-42
  Last Rites' effect, 39-40
  reactions to cardiac monitor, 29-34,
    36-37
  watching cardiac arrest, 37-38
Personality alterations, concentration
  camp survivors, 56
Phobias, 68-69
Physical discomfort, psychological
  effect, 75
Post-impact phase, emergencies, 68-69
Poverty, ghettos' effect, 58
Precognitions, disasters, 3-28
Precognitive experiences, 18 table
  Mark Twain, 4-5, 6
Pre-impact period, emergencies, 63-64
Premonitions bureaus, 25
  addresses, 26
Pre-set patterns, emergencies, 63
Preventive measures, combat fatigue, 82
Pseudocombat fatigue, 79
Psychiatric casualties
  reduction in Viet Nam, 83
  war situation, 70-71
Psychic adaptation, war situation, 73
Psychokinesis, 8, 13
Psychophysiological reactions,
  outer space, 86 table

R

Radiation, outer space experience, 87
Rationalization, threat reaction, 64-65
Reactions, uncertain threat
  situations, 64-65
Recoil phase, emergencies, 67-68
Red Cross, soldier's mental ills, 70
Regressive behavior, concentration
  camp effect, 53
Risk effect, space flight, 90-91
Russo-Japanese war, mental illness, 70

S

Sensitivity, precognitive dreams, 21-22
Sensory qualities, precognition, 15-17
Shell shock, 68, 71, 74
Social isolation, space flights, 89
Society for Psychical Research,
  see S.P.R.
Sociologists, studies of soldiers, 73
Soldiers
  mental illness, 70-72, 74-77
  neurotic, 80
  "nostalgia," 70
  preventing psychiatric difficulties, 82
  psychotic, 80
  social organization, 73
Space flight, psychological
  reactions, 86-92
S.P.R., 5
  precognition studies, 14-15
  precognitive dream cases, 17, 19
Stresses
  outer space, 86 table-92
  psychological responses, 73
Suicide, concentration camp
  infrequency, 55
Survival guilt, concentration camp
  results, 57
Symbolism, precognition, 17

T

Tektite project, 89
Theresienstadt concentration camp, 57
Thermal problems, space flight, 91
Threat uncertainty, reactions, 64-65
Time factor, emergency situations, 62-63
Titanic, 10
  precognitive dreams about, 18, 20,
    23-24
Traumatic neurosis, 58
Traumatogenic anxiety, concentration
  camp survivors, 59

U

Undersea mission, 89
United States
  military psychiatric aid, 72
  precognitive experiences, 22
University of Virginia, vii
U.S. Department of Health, 34